This book is due for return on or before the last date shown below.

26 JUN 1997

‑3 JUL 1999

27 JAN 1998

2 FEB 1999

0 3 MAY 2006

2 3 MAY 2006

- 1 DEC 2008

- 2 DEC 2008

6 DEC 2009
-4. MAY 2011

0 9 JUL 2012

2 2 APR 2015

Don Gresswell Ltd., London, N.21 Cat. No. 1208   DG 02242/71

PRACTICAL PIG-KEEPING

PRACTICAL PIG-KEEPING

DAVID BROWN

B.T. Batsford Ltd, London

Typeset by Servis Filmsetting Ltd, Manchester
Printed by the Bath Press, Bath, Avon
for the publishers
B.T. Batsford Ltd, 4 Fitzhardinge Street, London W1A 0AH
A catalogue record for this book is available from the British Library

ISBN 0 7134 6707 X

CONTENTS

PREFACE

After many years trying to drum the elements of good pig husbandry into raw though intelligent students it eventually became apparent that there must be a better way, if only to save repetition. 'Go and read so and so', I needed to say – but there was no 'so and so' to make them streetwise in the ways of swine, to instruct them in the art of driving a pig, to tell them which foot would suffer while they were trying to give a boar a helping hand. There were only tomes which told them what to do, but not how.

Hence a compendium of that which is not found in the usual works, with drawings to distract and delight the eye of those new to the pleasures of the pig.

7

INTRODUCTION

Pigs were ever scavengers, and they and their attendant swineherds have never been very highly regarded by the rest of agriculture. Even in Ancient Egypt they were considered impure, so much so that if you touched one you had to jump into the nearest river with all your clothes on. Herodotus tells us that swineherds were banned from the temples, and their daughters were unmarriageable outside the profession.

There is widespread evidence of domestic pig-keeping in Jericho in 8000 BC and from then on all over the Middle East. Around 5000 BC, Chinese pig-keepers were living fruitfully with their charges. These records include the size of herds and how much the different sizes of pig ate. Pork made up between 30–40 per cent of the total meat eaten in certain areas. There was a flourishing temple bureaucracy controlling the herds, and keeping a firm check on animal sacrifices to the gods.

However, sometime after 1000 BC the Muslim and Jewish prohibition against pork took effect and pigs vanished from the landscape. One theory that has a ring of truth to it is that this was due in part to the disdain of the aristocratic nomads for the town-dwellers and their sedentary animals.

In modern times, George Orwell's choice of Napoleon the pig in *Animal Farm* to parody Comrade Stalin continues the pattern, stressing the pig's cunning and greed. It's all a bit hard on the pig's image, but no other animal could have been moulded so exactly to the part.

The domestic pig is a descendant of the courageous and powerful wild boar, native of most of the Ancient World, even the islands of the east Indian Seas and the Chinese Empire. Mixed with British native breeds through centuries of agricultural improvement, the pig has achieved a remarkably complex genetic background. Black, white, blue and sandy Chinese were put in the genetic stew along with the native British, the Kentish, the Swing-tailed, the Scotch and the Devonshire – and these were just some of the small breeds. The larger breeds were just as diverse: the Cheshire, the Rudgewick (from the Sussex borders), the Yorkshire (commonly acclaimed as the worst), the Tonkey hog, the Tunback, a Kentish pig with a regular curvature of the spine, the Oxford, the Wiltshire and scores more.

The imported Chinese pigs and the subsequent Berkshire – softer, fatter and more succulent – were crossed with these hardy, indigenous breeds and provided a source of much-valued fat for a working population devoted to hard manual labour.

Wild boar have always been hunted by people, originally for food and subsequently for sport. Homer talks about the mountain boar: 'his eyes blaze fire, his tusks he whets the while, all eager to beat back both dogs and men.'

Baking in a mud wallow

Edward, Duke of York, wrote in the 1400s: 'It is a proud beast and fierce and perilous . . . for some men have seen him slit a man from knee up to the breast and slay him all stark dead at one stroke so that he never spake thereafter.'

In imperial India, the sport of boar-hunting probably reached its peak. It is recorded that one boar killed on the charge stood 1.2 m (4 ft) high at the shoulder and weighed 160 kg (350 lb). It's been all downhill since then. In America, the first attempt to promote wild boar- and sow-hunting with horse and spear was also the last. The hundred or so swine charged right through the novice hunters and high-tailed it for the mountains, taking large parts of the enclosing fence with them.

Wild hogs were with us until fairly recent times. Even in the 1850s, herds of them were living in the New Forest. These had been tampered with by Charles I, who brought over wild boar from Germany to improve the hunting. Their progeny had a fiery eye when excited but were reportedly very social animals, usually led by a large patriarchal boar. The Reverend William Gilpin, lying at ease under a beech tree, describes an encounter with them:

Suddenly a sound like that of warlike music mellowed by distance came upon our ears; we started so far up from our recumbent positions as to lean upon our arms and listen intently, and not without some degree of awe, being almost persuaded that some wondrous fairy pageant was about to gratify our sight; the sound grew harsher as it advanced; and as it [grew] nearer – yet nearer – the tramp of what might have been imagined to be elfin chivalry accompanied it. At length, while we were yet listening in mute anticipation, the leading boar of a large herd of forest pigs came grunting into view.

Whether it was the cheering, invigorating effects of the sunshine, or whether there was something particularly savoury in the herbage of that spot, we know not, but the grunting swelled into a loud chorus, their snouts became more and more busy, their ears and tails kept up one continuous and joyous motion and their small eyes seemed to flash back the sun's rays with unwonted eagerness of expression. Wishing to observe and admire them more closely, we sprang up, but in doing so alarmed them, and off they galloped helter skelter, *sauve qui peut*, with a speed that none of the porcine race not forest born and bred could equal; and long after every one was out of sight – vanished in the mazes of the woodland – we still heard their retreating trumpets, gradually dying away, until lost in the distance.

This is possibly the last description of this once-abundant wild race, although commoners of the New Forest still have rights of pannage to graze on acorns, chestnuts and beech mast. (The numbers allowed depend on the crop, to prevent hungry herds ravaging gardens.)

Lacking our universal and instant communications, every county and remote area preserved its husbandry peculiarities. In Kent, one commentator reports that as little milk was produced keeping swine was a matter of choice, attended with some difficulty. There was a table to work out the number of swine of different types that would consume the spare milk from a given number of cows. In Sussex, he noted that there was a practice of feeding a pint of salt to every two bushels of barley, fed dry to avoid waste. Yorkshire pigs, especially the Berkshire, were reported as remarkably quiet. In west Devon, no speying was done because there was no one skilled enough to perform the operation. The hogs were the original long, thin breed and spent their first three years on grass before being brought in to fatten. The fattening process was singular: they were shut in a narrow, closed hutch on a bed of mud and kept cool lest their fat melted.

Norfolk had as motley a mixture of breeds as anywhere, some people keeping far too many so that their half-starved hordes were a nuisance to their neighbours and 'no profit or pleasure to their owners'. The great Mr Bakewell was accused of improving the Norfolk breeds by incestuous intercourse, repeatedly returning successive generations of gilts to the same master boar.

The Highland pig was accused of being an ugly, brindled little monster, about the size of an English terrier which was the spitting image of a wild boar and roamed the moorlands. In Leicestershire, they made a stack of peas and beans as big as a cottage in a hedged yard near a brook, and turned the hogs in. This technique was used to fatten great numbers for London and to fill the salt-pork casks of the Navy. Another handy hint was to boil up hay and mix the meal with the juice. This reputedly had a profitable effect. Some people kept piglets with fatteners to clean out the troughs. If they survived, presumably they had the same service. One farmer built his pig yard round a stream to keep his animals clean and fresh; the comments of water-users downstream were not reported.

To illustrate that we don't get much cleverer, there is a report in 1837 of a Chinese pig farrowing three times in 18 months, producing 50 offspring. Elsewhere three litters every 16 months were achieved with up to 20 a litter not unknown and 13 and 14 common. A comment was made by the great Thomas Tusser to the effect that it is needful for the farmer to have some smattering of ordinary trades, and not to run to the carpenter or smith at every turn. His advice has been minded well ever since, especially by pig farmers who cannot normally afford outside experts and have become skilled master bodgers in the process.

In the sixteenth century, pigs were commonly used in towns as efficient scavengers, which must have added some interesting flavours to the meat. This continued in Ireland right up to 1824. Like the present urban fox, the urban pig was quite usual in eighteenth-century London and other cities. The large breweries in Battersea, Vauxhall and Wandsworth fattened 9000 pigs a year on waste from the beer-making process, and succulent pork it probably made. Nor were they kept just for food. A performing pig in Pall Mall in the 1790s drew profitable audiences – maybe it was the same one that had an insatiable appetite for herrings and would perform any antic to gratify it. There are also numerous records of sagacious pigs trained as gundogs, kept as pets, drawing carriages and riding in cars with their heads sticking out in the breeze. 'Pigs can see the wind', someone once said.

Pigs and opium seem to have a long-standing connection. I always thought reports of the Chinese transporting live hogs by popping a ball of opium in their mouths, stacking them up in junks and sending them peacefully downstream to the coast were apocryphal. However, Mr Dickson's excellent treatise on pigs, published in 1824, in which he uses the immortal subheading 'Improved Hoggery', comments that this practice is questionable and that overdosing of some hogs makes them so sleepy they will hardly rise to feed.

Apart from opium, many other products were, and are, eaten by pigs with enthusiasm. In the last war, they enjoyed Tottenham Pudding, great Christmas pud-like gobbets of nameless ingredients. In spite of appearances, though, in nature the pig is a delicate and discerning eater as long as he gets enough. Someone, Linnaeus I think, went to a peck of trouble to discover that in the wild the goat eats 449 plants and rejects 126, the sheep eats 387 and rejects 141, but the hog, 'more nice in its provision than any of the former', eats only 72 and rejects 171.

The sheer variety of pigs' diet in the 1720s is illustrated in *Mortimer's Husbandry*. Having had their morning feed of swill they were sent out to graze on moist, sedgey ground. Here they found hips and haws, sloes, crab apples, acorns, beech mast, beaten-down sycamore leaves and chestnuts, then back to their stone paved styes at night for another feed, where they could 'clean and air themselves'. The flesh from these animals was reputed very sweet. An unknown contributor to *The Compleat Farmer* reported: 'Their stomachs are well suited by nature to the reception of a great number of substances that are nourishing to them which in other circumstances must have been wasted or lost.'

The problems of slurry and smell are not new either; we just have more delicate nostrils now. Following the lack of night soil owing to the construction of sewers in the nineteenth century, a company was formed, the London Sewage Manure Company, which built works at Chelsea, of all places. A powerful pump was installed and raw sewage was propelled through 15 miles of pipe to market gardeners, who with hose and jet pipe supplied it where they pleased. The company was not a success but the celery, standing between trenches full to the brim, derived immense benefit from it.

There was also discussion on the various merits of top-dressing Hyde Park with manure and street refuse versus the same in liquid form, estimating that the escape of miasma would be less with the former. (Useful word, 'miasma', to impress motorists who complain if their windscreens are obscured by a brown film on good slurry-spreading days.)

Swineherds were never highly paid, a tradition that has been preserved. In twelfth-century Glastonbury, a good swineherd received one suckling pig a year and the entrails of the best pig slaughtered. Alternatively he could have the tails of all the pigs killed, which sounds a better bargain. By the late 1300s in Basingstoke, things had been put on a more professional basis, the going rate being $\frac{1}{2}$d per quarter per pig and an annual dinner from each tenant. On the other hand, swineherds had to sleep with the pigs and were responsible for any damage caused by them.

Some of the veterinary remedies in the eighteenth century and earlier were formidable. For catarrhal fever or distemper, the treatment was bleeding and the feeding of antimorial powder, 5–

6 grains, powder of contragjerva, 10 grains, with 2 drachms of liquorice powder.

Mortimer's Husbandry recommends the following for the gargol, which caused corruption of the blood from eating garbage and carrion, in hogs: bleed under the ears and tail, then a drink composed of rue, staverwort, hogs' madder and mayweed boiled in milk, which when cold has added to it a pennyworth each of treacle and sallet oil. It never failed.

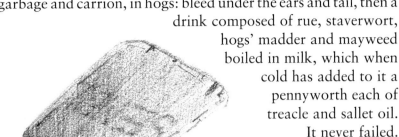

The rest will scatter with well-simulated cries of alarm

15

Ireland used to be one of the chief overseas suppliers of pigs to the English market, a place usurped today by Denmark and Holland. In the 1830s Ireland was a desperate place. The population, living almost exclusively on potatoes had nearly doubled in sixty years; such animals as they possessed had the same diet. Selling their pigs on the English market became one of the few ways to raise money. From 1821, when steam navigation across the Irish Sea began, the trade increased dramatically. By 1837, 600,000 pigs a year were coming into Liverpool alone. They were then sent by the Great Western Railway to Chippenham and driven in great herds to Calne where there was a huge bacon factory. Here they were turned into Wiltshire cure with not a word about their Celtic ancestry. The slow progress of the last stage of their pilgrimage caused much complaint among the local householders, but the art of petitions and lobbies was not so well developed then as now. However, the failure of the Irish potato crop and the Great Famine in 1845 meant that source of bacon disappeared.

A word now of explanation on the 'pig cycle', a phrase you will inevitably encounter. It has nothing to do with locomotion, but describes the cyclic nature of returns on pigs. Before we became Europeans, the cycle lasted about three years. Taking as a starting point a period when pig prices were high, enthusiasm and not unnatural greed persuaded producers to keep more breeding pigs in order to breed more pigs to make more money. When 10–12 months later, this flood of extra pigs hit the market, prices slumped. Those with big overdrafts or lacking in dedication sold out or cut down their herds, sales of breeding stock ceased and within another 10–12 months there was a dearth of pigs. Prices rocketed – which was where we came in.

The reason this cycle is peculiar to pigs is due to the enthusiasm with which they breed and their speed of growth. A cattle cycle would take decades and people would forget which part of it they were in.

Before we joined the EEC, the pig cycle was quite efficiently controlled, or at least tamed, by a band system that reduced prices when the national herd went over the danger limit and acted as a gentle but firm brake on excessive expansion. After we became members of the EEC, this was abandoned and we are now part of a vast European pig cycle. The results have not been beneficial, the old cycle of one good year, one reasonable and one poor having been replaced by two bearable, two dismal and two disastrous. It has, however, prevented a pork mountain, since no subsidy is or has been paid on pigs for decades, unlike sheep where the current subsidy equals the unsubsidized price, or arable farms from which pig farmers have had to buy their food at vastly above world prices. Nor have the butchers helped by holding up the price of pork when pigs are being given away. Strangely, this iniquitous system has produced no martyrs, no loads of slurry spread up Whitehall, merely a lot of grumbling, improved efficiency, deteriorating buildings and ex-pig farmers.

Do not place your faith in or expect any help or comfort whatsoever from governments of any hue, except in times of war, pestilence or famine. Pig farmers may be prime examples of the entrepreneurial spirit but electorally they don't count. You will succeed – if you do – in spite of them, and have a lot of fun doing it.

A PIG IN
THE GARDEN

You fancy keeping a pig in the garden, a start towards self-sufficiency? Maybe you think you might breed from it and start a mini-pig herd?

This first chapter is addressed to the complete novice and enthusiast – the most difficult person to advise. Any advice on pigs is subject to numerous qualifications and assumptions, which the hardened pig-keeper uses as seasoning to adapt to his own needs. If all these qualifications were spelt out, you would end up doing nothing so the following advice is fairly simple and does not spell out every possible course of action.

Keeping a pig in the back garden is part of a long and honourable tradition. The autumn-slaughtered pig was the principal bulwark between the farmworker's family and real hunger. Bought as a 'weaner' and fattened on any waste food, plus greenstuff from the hedgerows, barley meal and maybe skim milk, it was nurtured to an enormous size and fatness, for fat was relished in those lean times.

If this is your purpose, rather than keeping a pig as a pet, then it will satisfy all your self-sufficiency instincts, save you a lot of money and fill your freezer with delectable pork. You will also be astonished to find that you don't have to fill in a form or ask permission of anyone. If neighbours complain to the Health and Environment Officer, remember he will judge the case, firmly clutching the Public Health Act 1936, Section 92, on the basis of how it would affect a reasonable person.

So where will you put him – or rather them, for a pair will be company and probably grow better? Place their dwelling, with the reasonable person in mind, as far as you can from people, for we of the twentieth century have delicate nostrils and pigs can be noisy when anticipating food. A garden shed, 2 m (7 ft) square, will do at a pinch, as long as the floor is concrete and you have reinforced the inside with corrugated iron. Any edges of wood left exposed will be chewed.

The next essential is to insulate the floor, or at least where the pigs will sleep. This is easily done: put down a layer of 500-gauge polythene, 25 mm (1 in) of polystyrene, and about 40 mm (1.6 in) of concrete with a rough finish sloping gently to the door. The pigs will gain from that warm floor every time they lie down; you would be astonished how many livestock farmers still pay scant attention to insulating floors.

Pigs will eat anything

Finally, for the inside, put in a false roof. An old door will do, about 1 m (1 yd) above the floor against the end farthest from the door. Then block in half of the front of it so the pigs will have a cosy little cave with plenty of straw to sleep in away from the draught.

The outside run can be as large as you can afford, minimum roughly 3 × 2 m (10 × 7 ft), but it must be concreted unless you want them digging to Australia. There must be a step down into the run and a slight slope to take away the considerable quantities of rainwater and piddle that will accumulate. Put in a soak-away to take this and reduce any smell. You could put a roof right over the outside run and make it a lot more civilized for you and the pigs.

The run walls should be solid and over 1 m (1 yd) high, equivalent to 100mm blocks with buttresses, and the gate must have strong hinges and bolts top and bottom.

All these precautions will seem preposterous when you put in your two 30 kg (66 lb) pigs but they should grow very fast. Depending on a lot of variables, they will weigh 70 kg (154 lb) and be ripe for the freezer in another three months. One of these variables is what sort of pig you get. The simplest way to buy a pig is to ring up your friendly neighbourhood pig farmer and ask if you can buy two 30 kg (66 lb) boar pigs. You will want two of the same sex – they are precocious, and uncastrated boar pigs grow faster and leaner than gilts or females.

If you want gourmet pork, find a farmer with rare breed pigs like Berkshire or Gloucester Old Spot, and see if he has got any crossed with a modern meat boar. You will then have the best of both worlds: not too much fat but with fast growth and marbling of the meat to make the pork quite the best you have ever tasted. Rare-breed farmers are as much an endangered species as their stock, but they have a stand at most of the county shows.

About the only thing you need to do then is to get your pigs wormed and vaccinated against erysipelas and they should be fairly trouble-free, although this is not the sort of remark a seasoned pig-keeper makes lightly.

Pigs will eat nearly anything, but there are some things that you must not feed because they are illegal. In the old days, everything went into the pig bin, and swine fever and foot and mouth disease were endemic.

If you are a commercial pig farmer and you feed swill (in other words, waste food from hotels and restaurants), you are subject to a wad of regulations. This is because meat, even when it is cooked, can still hold some evil viruses, especially meat from abroad. The swill-feeder is resigned to living under this regime because he gets his food (for most people, 80 per cent of their total costs) at a minimal price.

Fortunately, you at the bottom of the garden are not subject to these rules, although you are still expected to boil any household waste for two hours at a minimum of 93.3°C. There is no check, but it would be civilized to do this rather than start an epidemic and get half the pig herds in the area slaughtered. The more robust self-sufficiency books extol the virtues of the pig bucket, into which go all plate scrapings and even the first rinsings of the washing-up. This may not fit the image of the modern kitchen but it does make for cheap and tasty pork.

Any vegetable matter except hemlock and deadly nightshade will find a ready appetite, especially as the pigs get bigger. There are all sorts of other waste foods available if you look around – stale bread and cakes for a start, though not if they have had any contact with meat pies! Check with your baker.

Pigs do, though, need something other than vegetable matter and stale bread to grow well, especially when young. Buying pig food in small quantities is very expensive. Try buying it from the person you got the pigs from, at bulk price. If the feed is in cubes or pellets (like nuggets and nearly as valuable), you can scatter these on the (clean) inside floor and you won't need a trough. If it is meal, mix it with warm water in winter; don't make it too sloppy. Feed to appetite twice a day – if they don't clear it up in half an hour, reduce the amount until they do.

One essential: you must have clean water always available. This sounds simple but is not unless you go to the expense of pipes and an automatic waterer. If you put in a monstrous cast iron trough, the pigs will walk and dung in it; if you use a light, easily cleaned trough they will tip it up within 30 seconds. The best compromise is a light, round trough fastened to the wall by a metal band, but so that you can take it out and clean it. This is a two-handed job and most pigs are still working on that one.

When you first get your pigs, you can carry them if need be, with a bit of noise and effort perhaps, but later you will need to guide and restrain (see Chapter 2). One regulation that must be strictly followed concerns animal movement licences. Any pigs that are moved from one property to another, unless their destination is a slaughterhouse, need a movement licence. This you can get from the local Ministry Licensing Officer whose telephone number every pig farmer will have handy. The regulation also applies to 'house-trained' Vietnamese pet pigs. If you take one on holiday, keep it away from other pigs or you will become distinctly unpopular.

Your total requirements for two pigs then, apart from the pen, will be around 10 bales of straw, which must be kept dry, and 200–300 kg (440–660 lb) of pig meal, depending on how big you take them and how much their diet is supplemented by juicy extras. You will also need a muck fork, a couple of troughs, pig boards (see p. 26), wellies, overalls and a sense of humour. Tolerant neighbours help. One last thing – don't give them names or they'll never end up in the freezer.

If you are thinking of breeding pigs in your garden, I can only say don't! However, if you're determined, here are some guidelines.

Notebooks containing the last 3 months' weighing results

The first thing that is likely to hit you is a polite enquiry from the local planning department about business planning permission and change of usage. On the technical side, it is difficult to know where to start. Even for two females, you will need a boar. It would be wildly expensive to buy a proper one; you could use artificial insemination (AI) but gilts (young females) are not easy even for experienced operators, or you could rear up a boar pig from the start with your two females and sell him at a loss. Immediately you get them in pig, the clock starts to tick and within four months you will need farrowing quarters, then weaner pens, sundry equipment, probably a vet – and what about a boar for next time, and a pen to put him in, and a few concrete paths?

If you do want to start in pigs on a small scale, this is not the way to do it unless your garden is larger and more isolated than most. Get a site or buildings where you can expand, and don't start with just any old pigs for these will determine your health status from then on and at this stage you probably don't know the right questions to ask.

If you really want pigs to keep you, then go and work for an efficient pig farmer to get experience and find out if you really like pigs. Choose a medium-size unit so you get to do all the jobs, stay for six months or a year and make your mistakes at his expense. Your motivation to learn will be valued. Ask a local vet who he suggests you apply to; he should have a pretty shrewd idea. A minimum size to produce a reasonable income as a one-man band is 100 sows, producing weaners, which will cost you the equivalent of a reasonable house to establish. All the time you are building up to this you will be spending more than you are getting back, because you are continually investing in new stock, which will not show any return for a minimum of eight to nine months. It is financially a very painful business, and it's a good idea to keep a job going at the same time.

When you are ready, cost your plans as realistically as you can, then halve the income, extend the time scale and put 50 per cent on your costs. Take your figures to an experienced pig-keeper and ask his advice, preferably in a period when prices are down so it is fresh in his mind what it's normally like. Draw up a two-year forward plan, independent of your bank manager's cash flow, to plan the accommodation you will need. It is a good idea to include odd small pens in which to put the ill, bullied or small, untidy groups. You always find these among older buildings but master plans sometimes miss them out.

More sage advice: don't be seduced into spending your precious capital or overdraft on shiny new equipment. Buy it cheaply second hand and clean it up well before you need it. It's a sobering thought to reflect why there is so much of it about. This principle is doubly true with buildings. As long as it is strong and warm and works, use whatever you can get. Plenty of straw bales will improve any building. Your ideas will keep changing; when you really know what you're doing, then spend money on buildings. You'll notice that most pig farms have at least one building they would like to alter.

DO	DON'T
Put your pigs as far from neighbours as possible.	Feed unboiled meat scraps.
Insulate the floor of the bed.	Forget pigs need a balanced diet to grow well.
Stop draughts.	Neglect to get an animal movement licence when they arrive.
Concrete the run.	
Look to your drainage.	
Make it all very strong.	Try and breed in a small garden.
Worm and vaccinate.	
Check the origins of your waste food and boil it where you can.	Get carried away and make optimistic forecasts.
	Spend your money on shiny new equipment.
Give them plenty of clean water.	
Get experience before you expand.	
Keep a job going as long as possible.	
Make your buildings cheap and cheerful.	
Have fun.	

DIARY

Friday 1st of January: Feeding in the cold.

The first day of another year. Friday it may be, but after a three-day break it's like Monday, only more so.

An office or factory sits there from Friday night quietly waiting and causing no pain to anyone. On a pig unit the normal biological functions take no heed of holidays and go on relentlessly. There are fewer people about, the pigs get bored and mayhem blossoms.

When you start feeding after a break, you can be confident that some unseemly sight will meet the eye – a boar pen door swinging open or a reposeful, lifeless body. It's cold today too, a keen east wind with flecks of snow. The outside taps will be frozen solid and exposed troughs will have lumps of half-chewed ice in them. You've drawn the short straw, and everything needs bedding and warming up and the farrowing crates will need a proper going-over.

It's highly probable too that one or two of last week's weanings will perversely be on heat in spite of having been weaned late on purpose – leave that until later in the morning.

All you feel this morning is a faint superiority over those still abed and a background headache from over-indulgence. You certainly don't feel your feet, which became lifeless an hour ago, or much enthusiasm. Speed on the first breakfast of the year.

A mobile ad-lib feeder

MOVING
AND LOADING

Pig-driving is an art form, not easily acquired. It needs agility, forethought, much quicker reactions than the normal (non-piggy) person has, an IQ marginally above that of the pig, and a deep and affectionate knowledge of pig response and psychology. It also resembles medical practice in that on occasion it is important to do nothing and stand perfectly still.

Designed by nature to be able to force its way through thorn, thicket and jungle, with a turn of speed and ability to feint and swerve that an England three-quarter might envy, pigs are a formidable challenge to guide. The only things on your side are that you control the terrain – usually – and that their stamina is limited, though this may well apply also to the guider!

There are different techniques for different sizes and groupings, but the first essential is to reduce the odds because there are usually more pigs than people. Start by blocking all possible escape outlets along the desired route with something solid and definitely opaque, fixing it so that it does not fall flat with a bang in a puff of wind at a crucial moment. Enterprising pigs will make for any new gap, the rest will scatter with well-simulated cries of alarm, and you will be left with the classic convoy commodore dilemma, needing immediate action, with a 50 per cent chance of being right.

The well-run pig unit has permanent hinged gates and hurdles; the rest use old sheets of tin or whatever is lying handy. Each driver should be equipped with a 'pig board'. A properly made one is essential: 60 cm (2 ft) square, three-eighths exterior ply, with a smooth hand-hole and the bottom two edges rounded off. Try to make it yourself – one from a feed firm will cost a fortune in food orders and will probably be too flimsy. A board of this size and weight can be used in a high wind and can also accompany the bearer if he needs to run fast (which is probable), unlike a large sheet of rusty corrugated iron.

Finally, the company should all be in agreement as to where the pigs are going and be restrained from too much hullabaloo of the 'Hey! Hey!' variety, which only serves to convince the pigs that something alarming and unpleasant is about to happen. A slightly hectoring conversational tone is suitable.

They will try to turn round . . .

27

A group of large, adult females, not more than 15, is probably the easiest group to move, especially if they are used to being driven and amenable to chat. Try, though, to stop them from going the wrong way up a narrow one-way passage – pigs cannot back up easily, so they will try to turn round and will jam themselves in a tight 'U' shape. I have no advice on this problem, except demolition.

If the sows have been closely confined in a farrowing crate, after a few hesitant steps they may well go 'woof, woof' and take off like a rocket. Or, if they are strangers, some will square up and start battling, while the timid ones will flee in several directions. A resounding wallop with the flat of the board on the head of the fighters will usually startle them apart. If not, run the pig board between their heads but don't follow it through.

How to carry a pig

Grown fattening pigs are more of a challenge and are very susceptible to the 'woof, woof and away' syndrome. They weigh around 90 kg (200 lb) and are equivalent to healthy young adults of 18. With a group of perhaps 30 such pigs, it might be helpful to have a swift volunteer to go in front, like the man with the red flag, to slow them down. How he does it is up to him.

Smaller pigs in groups of 20 to 50 are different again. They can't see as far, and if one or two separate from the group and panic, the group's progression will resemble a typhoon going round in circles, but forward and hopefully in the right direction. It's probably better to let them go; they won't go far and can be rounded up later. You'll do better catching them by the ears and tail and carrying them back. It's hard work driving a solitary weaner.

Smaller pigs also need more vocal guidance. They tend to be less adventurous and more apprehensive, and you just have to accept that it is going to take longer. Pigs, you must remember, are not on the human time-scale treadmill and regard being hustled as human bloodymindedness.

More time is also necessary with the highly pregnant sow brought in to farrow. She will have spent four expensive months getting to her weighty and vulnerable condition, so let her proceed at her own ponderous pace. If she exercises her pregnant status and just won't go through the right doorway, try luring her with food, take her another way or give her time.

Moving single pigs is often more difficult than a covey. If the pig is amenable and you are reasonably agile, station yourself astern. If you want it to go left, move up on the starboard quarter, and vice versa. If the beast is a fast-moving escapee, two drivers are useful, one on each quarter. If, however, you are outrun don't throw your board ahead of it in a desperate attempt to stop it. If you succeed in checking it by an Olympic throw, it will only run back past you while you retrieve your board from a pool of mud.

It takes six to eight weeks of constant pig work to develop the necessary reaction speed and intuition. After about 20 years you get quite good at it, but by then you can't run.

Never completely trust an adult boar, however docile he is normally; if you can, have two people to drive him. Don't drive him near any penned boars, and make absolutely sure that no other boar is being moved at the same time. If he does get upset and starts chumping his jaws and pawing the ground, don't stay and argue unless you're experienced and can run.

Loading pigs on to transport is a continuation of the usual problems of moving them, with a few extra added. Basically, you are funnelling them on to a ramp and into what is to them a strange and frightening pen, often uphill. If they are for slaughter, they should be split into manageable groups of 20 or less and the aim is to keep them flowing steadily. If the group is too big and the front ones out of reach, they may turn back and make a solid, noisy and unhappy log-jam. If you have an exprienced 'driver', take your cue for maximum effort from him. If he is new and excitable, restrain him. The knowledge of when to do absolutely nothing is vital. To 'whoosh' up a pig that has just decided to go anyway is usually a mistake, as he will then realize he's being coerced and put up a struggle.

How not to carry a pig

A very useful aid to driving pigs up a ramp on to the top deck is to use straw to block up the airholes in the sides of the lorry adjacent to the ramp. Although you know that pigs cannot fall through a 15×30cm (6 in $\times$ 1 ft) gap, pigs do not share your conviction. Much heaving, shouting and bad language can be avoided by this simple artifice, but only some lorry drivers and no lorry body manufacturers are aware of it. Weaners, even more than slaughter pigs, do not take kindly to ramps; as in driving them, everything takes a little longer and should be allowed to do so.

Larger pigs, sows and boars either go up like a dream or, if they can't be bribed with food, you lean on their rear ends until one of you has had enough. They have a lot of patience. Another method is to back a large pig up the ramp with a bucket held over its head, but watch your fingers.

Boars are inherently suspicious and don't easily fit into the role of pushee. If you have a sow, put her on first; if she's on heat, a boar will follow. You only have one chance though; if he gets off, forget it, so no fumbling with shutting hurdles behind him.

Incidentally, do not think that because it's taken half the morning and all your week's ration of energy to load up a lorry that the pigs will rush to get off at the other end. Loading conditions, including temperature, can be a matter of life and death. In hot weather, load pigs early, with a minimum of uproar and before they are fed. Pigs live in a fat overcoat and can only lose heat by conduction; they cannot sweat. If they become overheated and stressed, they will quickly die. You will then have a tedious and probably unproductive argument over whose insurance covers what. Pig producers should bear in mind that they spend up to five months and much time, money and skill rearing pigs in optimum conditions, and when slaughter day comes what happens? They are bundled on to a lorry, fight, experience maximum stress with strange pigs for several hours, are unloaded and kept for up to 24 hours under, to them, fairly bleak conditions, and then slaughtered. It is an arguable point that as much care should be given pigs during the delivery and slaughter period as when they are on the unit, both from the point of view of profit and humane considerations.

Now to the merry sport of weighing. In many abattoirs the weight bands are as the laws of Moses and half a kilo over or under loses a lot of money per pig. It is essential to weigh before despatch. Put like this, weighing sounds very reasonable, but it can be one of the most arduous jobs unless planned properly. You are proposing to put independently minded pigs, probably weighing as much as you do and as strong as you are, into a crate about 1.5×0.5 m ($5 \times 1\frac{1}{2}$ ft). Even with a 100-sow herd, you will be weighing 40 to 60 pigs a week, including last week's rejects. Each pig is fresh and fit, and as the morning drags on you will become progressively more tired and filthy and, unless you have a saintly disposition, more irritable. But, before you go right off the whole idea, it can be made a little easier.

First, there are the weighing scales. If you inherit a set you may be able to adapt it, but if you buy a set, new or second hand, there are certain points to watch for. Ensure that it has a door catch that is pig-proof and doesn't spring back smartly and agonize your knee-cap while the backward-released swine runs over your feet. Check for rust traps along the bottom edges (few substances are as corrosive as pig urine) and that the floor is replaceable; also that it is capable of being dragged about without undue effort and that the weighing head has an efficient damper.

They have a lot of patience

Finally, if you have to read ear numbers, ensure that the height of the framing on the top strikes a fine balance between giving the pig the idea that it can escape through the roof, or having your fingers crushed between its head and a cat's cradle of bars.

Now for the actual weighing. Your aim is to get the pig in the scales with the least effort and damage to you both. Assuming that your reactions are now as fast as the average swine, to achieve your aim you will need to use a little guile.

Take a pig away from his group and propel him towards, but past, a strange machine for which he feels no affection. The way to get him in is to offer him the chance to rejoin his mates by going back through the scales – which he will do rapidly and triumphantly if you forgot to secure the far end door. (A word in passing – keep alert if you're standing among a group containing gilts. They pee backwards and you could have a warm, wet welly.)

As an alternative to all this, the Americans have a tradition of calling their pigs – 'hog-calling'. They even have contests and championships in the art. The callers are judged on strength of tone (which must be sweet and friendly so that it doesn't impede the hog's digestion), originality of call (so you get your own hogs), variety (to avoid boredom and moodiness), persuasiveness (to entice the pig from whatever it's currently doing) and finally the hint of command. Bucket-rattlers are regarded as beyond the pale, but there was a school that had some success with the old-fashioned motorhorn. However, this was rapidly abandoned after the discovery of numerous herds of hogs scattered about the Midwest, unable to keep up with honking cars.

So you've moved and loaded your pig or pigs. Where are you sending it or them? If you have one or two pigs from the end of the garden your options are fairly simple. If you want them for yourself, send them to a small local abattoir and get a friendly local butcher to joint them until you learn how.

Alternatively you can sell them to the same butcher or put them in the nearest market. But unless pigs are in great demand your locally unknown pigs won't make you a fortune. It would be better to buy a second hand deep freeze and sell surplus joints privately to your friends.

If you have groups of pigs to sell, enquire which is the best procurement group in your area. They will guide your infant footsteps and ensure that they go to the best abbatoir for your size and type of pig. Talk to them about insurance on the lorry, what happens if the abbatoir suddenly goes bankrupt, how long before you get paid and killing-out percentages between abbatoirs. Finally, even if it seems a lot of trouble, go regularly and see your pigs on the hook. Once you become known for this eccentric behaviour your pigs will be watched to make sure they are treated properly. By the time you have waved the lorry goodbye you will have invested a great deal of time, care, energy, thought and money in them. It's a good idea not to relax and wait for the cheque. Make sure you are getting all that's due.

DO	**DON'T**
Reduce the odds.	Shout and wave your arms about.
Prepare the route.	
Get the right equipment.	Drive sows up a narrow one-way passage.
Use pig boards.	
Agree where the pigs are going.	Try and drive small, isolated pigs.
Split pigs for loading into manageable groups.	Ever trust an adult boar.
Restrain excitable drivers.	Let pigs get stressed and overheated.
Let pregnant sows go at their own pace.	Let gilts pee down your boots.
Load early in hot weather.	Let pigs run on icy concrete.
Get the right weighing scales.	

DIARY

Tuesday 19th of January: Loading pigs on the lorry.

It's one of the immutable laws of nature that it starts to rain at 6.55 on loading mornings. The only exception is when it snows. The lorry comes at 7.

We arrive at 6.40 at the fattening houses to give us time to assemble the pigs before our old friend Chicka backs his lorry up the drive, at 7 a.m., in a cloud of diesel. By then, we should have 40 baconers careering up and down the concrete.

It's a harsh way to start the day, for us and the pigs. Those due for bacon were marked with a cross at yesterday's weighing, and I clutch the precious sheet written out last night showing which pen they are in.

Two of us work down each side, one holding the pen gate, the other selecting out the chosen ones, while their mates watch enviously as they gallop out on to the concrete.

. . . before the rest turn and avalanche down again

Once assembled, we consult with Chicka as to how he wants them loaded. 'Twenty on the top deck', he announces, which is hard work. This is the price we pay for having the empty lorry come to us first.

We open the ramp gates, cut out the nearest 20 and drive them onto the platform ready to go. The rain has hesitated and stopped. There is a pause while one of us puts a permanent 'slap mark' on each pig to mark them as ours, then, at the word from Chicka, speed them all together down the passage and with a lot of encouragement up the lorry ramp to the top deck. Our driver is vastly experienced and knows to a second when to exhort them to move. They all go up like a dream, except one – there's always one – and we have to push and half-carry him up in frantic haste before the rest turn and avalanche down again. The ramp forms part of the top deck, so if they do we'll be lifting a heavy hinged floor plus several hundred kilos of mobile pig.

We get the laggard safely aboard and go back, hot and panting gently, to fetch the rest, dipping our boots in disinfectant as we go, having been on hostile lorry territory. The rest are easy, going in on the level and we wave them off with relief and a slight feeling of Judas. Alter the feed charts, switch on the automatic feeder with a silent prayer that it works, and back to the rest of the feeding. Loading, calling as it does for sudden effort and maximum adrenalin, is an energy-sapping business leaving you a bit flat till after breakfast, but today it went well.

The next job is to move every pig up one pen to make room at the bottom of the pile for the babes weaned last week. An empty pen on a pig farm is a contradiction in terms.

THE PIGS
ARE OUT

Keeping pigs, as opposed to losing them through holes in the boundary, can be time-consuming if you don't appreciate their abilities. Pigs escape even on the best-run farms at all sorts of odd times though more often, it seems, in the evening or on a Sunday afternoon. This is when they are not only bored through lack of human contact, but have worked out that there isn't anyone about. Pigs are designed by nature to squeeze through thicket, thorn hedge and undergrowth, and the lure of freedom and the curiosity to explore new horizons make any chance to escape irresistible.

There are four basic procedures for dealing with a mass break-out. First, concentrate the pigs. If you are dealing with teenage delinquents or adult stock, rattle a bucket and fling meal or cubes among the largest group, especially if you are alone. Treat them like a fire: one bucket now is worth a fire engine in half an hour.

If you are dealing with weaners, they have probably been fed *ad lib* and freedom will seem more interesting than grub. However, they won't go very far or fast in a straight line as a group, though single adventurous specimens may turn up hours later in odd places. In-pig sows on the loose, or worse, on-heat sows, will go for miles given the chance. Boars are more predictable. They either try to kill another boar through a gate with much foam and crashing and gnashing of teeth, or hang hopefully round the gilt yard. Either way, they're sexed-up and dangerous, so make sure you know how to deal with them (see

Much foam and crashing and gnashing of teeth . . .

Chapter 11). At this early stage, it's also not a bad idea to check that the escapees are in fact your very own pigs, not some disease-ridden strangers. Knowing where most of the pigs are and will be for a minute or so, run round and check that all the perimeter gates and gaps are closed. Next summon help and accumulate the pig-driving equipment. Have some recognized whistle, bell or rattle to alert people if any of several sorts of disaster strike. You should probably also have shouted more often about the pig boards being returned to the right place and not left where they were last used, usually by the loading ramp.

Finally, before you start the round-up, find out whence the pigs came. This is not always as easy as it sounds: a shattered gate or swinging door are easy enough, but a metal sheet that springs back after the pigs have squeezed out can baffle the keenest observer. Although it is preaching perfection and quite improbable in practice, a spare pen to put pigs in while you sort things out is invaluable, especially if more than one group are out and start fighting. As strangers invariably fight you will have groups trying to kill each other in every direction.

There are variations on these themes. If you keep tame pigs like Gloucester Old Spots, they tend to run towards you when you appear, especially if you're in the habit of taking them hedging or for rides in the front of your van. If you meet 30 weaners on your nightly walk-round and it's summer, shut all the gates and go to bed. If, on the other hand, you meet an uneasy sow in the dark, she will probably be so relieved she'll follow you to the nearest lit doorway. But if you're sitting behind your perimeter fence smug in the knowledge that your pigs can't go far, don't relax. Are you sure someone hasn't let a sow wander about thinking all the gates to the outside world are shut?

Another interesting variable is the solitary, obviously suckling piglet wandering about very sad in the vicinity of the farrowing house. Mum has probably lifted him out of the crate with her nose by accident. You then have to match him for size, count them all up and hope you have got it right.

We once searched high and low for a sow that had broken out, scented the food in the trough in the next crate which held a litter of newly weaned piglets and clambered in, bearing out the old maxim that if you want to vanish stay on your home territory and blend into the background.

First, concentrate the pigs

Chatting up the gilts in the gilt yard

DO	DON'T
Concentrate them. Close the perimeter. Get help and equipment. Have a good alarm system. Find where they came from. Keep checking the perimeter fence.	Panic. Leave pig boards scattered around. Give yourself a coronary.

DIARY

Thursday 25th of February: Weaning the sows.

Straight after breakfast, we set forth with pig boards and enthusiasm to wean this week's sows. First job, rig up hurdles to hold them in a congregating area as we back them out of their farrowing crates.

The first three back out with a little guidance, pulling their emerging tails round to line them the right way up the passage, then they 'whoof' off up the concrete like air-to-air missiles. When they stop to draw breath, two of them instantly start a ferocious fight. The next one due out is reluctant to come; possibly she trod on one of her offspring and feels remorse. We've got her half out, bent like an 'L' when the non-fighting member of the trio comes strolling down the passage again. In the uproar of ejecting her backwards, the difficult one slides back in her crate again. Hey ho!

Fighting with joyful fury

When all 10 are out and half are fighting with joyful fury, we drive them round to the sow pens with noisy banter and thankfully slam the gates on them.

They then get a slap-up feed to reduce the aggression entailed in deciding who is boss in the new grouping and we go back to give the newly bereaved piglets some tender loving care, more warmth and food and extra straw to play with. Not that they give a damn at the moment, they're too busy racing round in the extra room created by the absence of Mother. We leave them in peace to get over their first big trauma. A quick look to see that the sows have settled; it's 9.30 and time to start the day proper.

HUSBANDRY

Good husbandry is the magic ingredient in all livestock farming; without it you are just going through the motions. It is manifest if your pigs are content and performing well.

People who are brilliant with machinery seldom have this quality in high degree and, conversely, people who are good with animals are often mechanically illiterate. A good husbandman needs the instinctive ability to put himself mentally in the pig's place. You may be working hard, be warm and think it's a lovely winter's day but pigs lying in the shade unable to avoid an Arctic draught would be of a different opinion. This sympathetic ability often seems to be inherited. It can be taught but the best seem born with it.

Hemsworth and Barnett in Australia have done years of work on the human-pig relationship and, unlike a lot of research psycho-babble, it makes fascinating reading. They studied the implications and effects of the closer relationship between humans and pigs since intensive farming was introduced. Taking the level of fear of humans to reflect the quality of the relationship, they measured how long it took a pig to approach an observer who was standing still. (What they didn't mention is that some strains of swine become overly familiar quickly, while others take a lot of getting to know – like humans.)

They also split the pigs into groups: those that were pleasantly handled, hardly handled at all or treated with arbitrary bad

43

temper, both on their research unit and on commercial farms. The pigs in the badly treated group grew a lot slower than the others; they didn't conceive as well and the boars took longer to get their act together on both the unit and the farms.

However, you don't have to beat pigs to slow down their growth. With smaller pigs, if you stride about erect wearing gloves they take this to be threatening behaviour and grow slower and more expensively. If you crouch bare-handed and stay still you're a friend, but you don't get much work done.

If you are nice to them Monday to Thursday and kick them around on Friday, they remember and stay stressed, with results similar to those that have continual unpleasant treatment. This has an obvious message for large units with several staff. At a large research station, 2000 pigs completely stopped growing for a week and the only change in treatment or management was a relief stockman. He was a good stockman but he sounded, looked, smelt and acted differently.

Sows are unhindered by mud

Every good stockman knows he has to be gentle and understanding to animals to get the best out of them, but pigs' degree of sensitivity to handling revealed by this research has deep implications as to how we should keep them in the future. It is now possible to quantify kindness in terms of cash, and it may be that agricultural colleges will be asked to provide diploma courses in pig psychology and husbandry as well as teaching the mechanics of the trade.

Generally, the smaller the pig the greater the susceptibility to stress. The smallest they'll be is in the womb, then after birth and suckling (see Chapter 12) the next crisis point is weaning. A lot of husbandry is reducing or removing stress and this is probably the biggest stress point in any pig's life.

In the wild, weaning happens when mother and offspring get mutually fed up with each other and the litter starts getting independent, usually when they are about eight to ten weeks old. Also the milk bar runs dry and she starts thinking about the next generation. We have reduced this point progressively to three weeks and younger, and for the piglets this can be a shattering experience. Suddenly their source of warmth, comfort, protection and food vanishes, so it behoves you to do all possible to lessen the blow. Double the warmth for a week – they often suffer severe temperature loss and lose body fat fast. Make sure the creep is warm, strawed, comfortable and draught-free. Disturb them as little as possible and, above all, make sure the food and water are right, clean and plentiful. The trauma in the gut is as violent as the emotional one, while the enzymes used to a diet of milk struggle with an influx of carbohydrates, but this will be eased if they have had access to food well before weaning.

Stress is also lessened if you can avoid mum treading on any of her offspring as she backs out of the crate and departs at a high rate of knots with never a backward glance.

Watch the piglets like a hawk for the first few days. They may have started to grow and have recovered from or avoided any weaning check, but until now they've been in litter groups of nine or ten. The next stress peak is mixing them in larger 'even' groups. You may have already let several litters run together while they were still suckling; there is a temptation to mix them in huge groups of 40–50, economizing on space, but any kind of mixing causes maximum stress and a severe check and if it is possible to leave them in litter groups, and even in the same pen, there is evidence of a considerable improvement in all-round performance. If the mother is returned to spend her next pregnancy with them, eating separately, there is yet further gain, a system that Geoffrey Johnson was pioneering in the 1960s.

On most farms space, labour and established buildings forbid this approach but when you do mix piglets don't go over around 30. Although the biggest and the weakest in the group soon establish a pecking order over 30, those in the middle find it increasingly difficult to remember all these strange faces and smells and never know who to defer to. This results in a general low level of bickering and discontent, resulting in outbreaks of violence with an unhappy effect on growth. They also have a nasty habit of dying back to the level the accommodation will sustain.

Another point, often neglected, is that even with 30 pigs you need three or four automatic waterers spread separately; one will not do. Thirty reasonable humans could manage with one source, you think, so why not pigs, but the weaker ones will not get enough water and will fall further behind.

It's not only growing pigs that are affected by stress and shock; sows can be severely stressed as well. The usual practice at weaning is to group the batch of sows together, where they fight and bite and the weaker and probably most productive ones become pretty miserable, compounding the emotional upset and swollen tender udders. What they really need is warmth, solitude and peace, which could well be repaid by much better performance.

Boredom afflicts us all occasionally and swine are convivial beasts, given in the wild to rooting and foraging with their strong, inquisitive noses, so being crowded together on bare concrete is not for them an attractive place to be. Good food *ab lib* reduces the boredom factor. Give them plenty of straw to chew and a lot of problems will fade away. It benefits their digestion and well-being and they will eat a huge amount, given the chance.

Talking of food, back in the 1870s in Germany and the Tyrol, pig-fattening was very simple and economical, according to the remarkable Mrs Beeton in her footnotes to the 'Pork Cutlet' section of her book. At dawn, she tells us, the swineherd would crack his whip and the pigs of the village would pour out and follow him to the next village, hamlet or house, where the process would be repeated until he had several thousand pigs milling about. Thereupon he would set forth up into the mountains to a fresh feeding area and make a shelter for himself until twilight, when he gathered them together again and returned them to their respective abodes. The drover would then 'seek his cottage and repose'.

Another pig farmer who had it organized was Sir James Colquhoun of Luss. He used to ship his pigs across to an island on Loch Lomond every autumn, where they were no trouble to anyone and fattened sweetly on acorns in oak groves, which gave a surprising delicacy to the flesh.

Today, computerized automatic feeding and transponders have taken the fun out of pig nourishment, except when they blow up on Sunday mornings. There is currently a trend to go back to keeping sows outdoors again as in our youth. In the summer it's easy, the ground is fairly dry and there's grass to eat, but it's a different matter dispensing food to 30 or 40 hungry sows full of adrenalin and charging about in a sea of mud. Sows are relatively unhindered by mud and don't leave their wellies behind and squelch around in their socks.

A word on troughs, hoppers and stress – yours and the pigs. Portable troughs vary from round cast iron monsters that can be

Sow cultivating meadow

wheeled like hoops but break your leg if they slip and are immoveable in mud to galvanized ones that will rust and high-grade plastic that will save your back but break your bank manager's heart. Similarly with hoppers. Try and pick feeders where the food actually reaches the pig's stomach. Concrete troughs are not as simple and obvious as they look so get some expert advice before you make your ideas permanent, and always be generous with trough space.

A word, too, on automatic feeding systems. Once installed, they usually preclude any form of easy hand-feeding so make absolutely sure that mechanics can and will attend you at any hour of the day or night, not excluding Bank Holidays, Christmas Day or their daughter's wedding.

Pigs come naturally encased in an envelope of fat, the thickness depending on how genetically superior they are. This is fine in cold weather but when it gets hot pigs can be in trouble because they can't sweat. They do actually have a couple of little holes inside each foreleg unknown to many vets but it doesn't signify because no one seems to know their purpose. They depend on conduction to loose heat with preferably some convection thrown in. A mud wallow in a cooling breeze is the ideal solution. Failing that, anything of similar consistency will do, hence the pig's unjustified reputation for being mucky. If they can't do this, then they overheat and eventually die; hot, irritable pigs tend to fight and again

A mud wallow in a cooling breeze

you can get bodies. Make especially sure you keep farrowing and suckling sows cool in a heatwave, and load your pigs early in the cool of the morning with the minimum of fuss.

If you find a stressed, overheated pig, don't douse it with ice cold water or it may have a heart attack. Pour water on the ground and let it wallow, provide shade and a flow of air, and put wet sacks on it. Don't force it to move. If it still looks as if it's going to die, there is an injectable heart stimulant that your vet can provide for you to keep in stock.

In pig terms, the pecking order means that the boss pig dominates number two, and he orders about number three, and so on down the line to the weakest who only speaks when he's spoken to. It does mean everyone knows their place, discipline is maintained and you get fewer outbreaks of rioting and hooliganism. If you take the boss pig out, unless he goes back within a short time he has to fight for his throne all over again. Crowd pigs in large numbers and restrict their feed, and they'll fight and get aggressive – as you would.

Keep looking at your pigs until the look of a normal pig is imprinted on your subconscious so that you are able automatically and without thinking to pick out the odd, the unusual, the ill one and the one that is going to be ill tomorrow. While you are looking, remember Winston Churchill's shrewd observation that dogs look up to you, cats look down on you but pigs look you in the eye like an equal.

The recognition of the various noises that pigs make is a crucial part of husbandry. In spite of being often intolerable, to the trained ear noise is always informative and often vital. At one extreme is the inferno of uproar, well above the decibel pain level of a fattening house earnestly desiring food. At the other, the mournful 'cheep-cheep' of a lost and despairing baby piglet, its pathos discernable to the experienced ear even through background noise. It is slightly more difficult to distinguish between the piercing shrieks of a litter of suckling piglets fighting for the best teat and the equally piercing shrieks of a piglet being crushed by several hundred pounds of mother. The voice of the latter, however, usually has that little extra tonal something that induces you to get up and leave the warm office to go and have a look.

There is the staccato warning bark of the first pig in a startled group to sight danger, or the chance for a bit of fun. The whole lot freeze as one – then, infinitely slowly, they come to life, then again, suddenly, as one pig they return to normal. Each one, however, has his eye on you. Then there is the low-key ecstasy of a contented sow suckling a newborn litter, the screaming outrage of a weaner being picked up and taken he knows not where by he knows not whom, and the exuberant 'woof-woof' of a covey of excited swine breaking into a gallop.

The rapid 'huh-huh-huh' of a boar chatting up a would-be compliant sow is often the first indication of a break-out. The querulous long, drawn-out reproach of a sow having her stomach walked over at 3 a.m. sometimes reaches the level where it wakes you up with a start. Some pig noises are very difficult to evoke, like the low pitched gasping noise that means a sow has tried to do a somersault in a crate, has jammed its head and is rapidly going blue.

Similarly, the other odd type of noise that is out of place, the breathless, scuffling noise that means there is a fight going on.

All these noises have a useful message, but one not often heeded is that noise over a certain decibel level – as from a hungry fattening house – can permanently damage your hearing. Be professional and wear ear protectors.

DO	**DON'T**
Put yourself mentally in the pig's place.	Stress pigs, especially at peak stress periods like weaning.
Give extra warmth at weaning.	Mix in large groups.
Watch the weaned pigs closely for the first week.	Forget your effect on the pig.
Give more than adequate access to water.	Use troughs or systems that waste food.
Treat your sows gently at weaning.	Let your own hearing be destroyed by default.
Remember outdoor pig-keeping has problems too.	
Keep pigs cool in hot weather.	
Avoid icy draughts	
Study the pecking order.	
Check the back-up for high tech feed systems.	
Look at your pigs all the time.	
Learn the different noises and what they mean.	

Look out . . . here he comes

DIARY

Friday 11th of March: The wet-feed unit blows up.

It's a grey morning. Walk up the drive to the fattening unit, unlock the mealhouse door and switch on the automatic wet feed unit to circulate. The sound of the pump also switches on the nearest pigs to breakfast wavelength and a crescendo of noise up to 120 decibels spreads rapidly through the four houses.

Give it four minutes, press the 'start' button and walk to the far end to watch all is well.

Disaster! As you open the door of the last house, a great flood of porridge is washing up the passage towards you like Vesuvius. The first pen is already flagging at trying to keep up with this monstrous largesse, but the other troughs are bare. The decibel level rises to 130.

Race back to the feed unit to switch off and stare in fury at the array of electronics, then roar off in the van back to the main unit to get help, stilsons and a quick cup of coffee in lieu of breakfast. Back, and the houses have settled down to a brooding, discontented muttering.

The decibel level rises to 130

First step, bucket-and-shovel up the passageful of porridge and give some to every pen in this house at least, while we start to track down the probable blockage. Set to with large spanners and small ladders, undoing the joints in the overhead pipes and poking a running hose up each one. As well as clearing any blockage, this keeps you cool by running a stream of dilute porridge down your upstretched arm and into your wellies. At long last, the pipe seems clear. We connect up the last joint and switch on again. The sound of the pump galvanizes the thousand swine once more, now two hours hungrier, as we stride confidently back to the beginning. Nothing – the valve has stuck.

With quiet fury in a gale of noise, we attack corroded screws with hacksaws and replace the valve, but all is forgiven as it effortlessly feeds – sweet music.

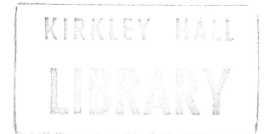

SHOPPING FOR FOOD

A ll relaxed, non-active pig farmers can skip this bit; the vagaries and villainies of the feedstuff trade can be tedious. For the unfortunate remainder, for whom food can be 80 per cent of their total costs, it's a matter of some importance.

Point No. 1 is to trust nobody until you're confident that you're dealing with one of the vast majority of suppliers who are honest. Having established that, make sure that you get on well with whoever you deal with because you are going to try his patience sorely with a lot of awkward questions and generally be thoroughly difficult.

Make sure that he'll agree to his food being checked by an independent analyst. He'll be covered by insurance for unwitting mistakes, so if he's honest but incompetent he won't mind. He should be willing and able to answer questions on any product and provide answers within a couple of days, and also be prepared to keep in contact weekly.

The firms you meet may have discovered the equivalent of alchemy in producing pig food, but beware of people who violently undercut normal prices. In this trade, as in most others, you get exactly what you pay for and if you demand a cheap ration you'll get one. Beware, too, of offers to take you out to expensive lunches. The business is very competitive and one way or another you'll be paying for every mouthful.

There are a number of traditional and time-hallowed methods by which you could be cheated. The moisture content may be made to rise by several expensive per cent. Make sure it's on the quote and then have it checked. Very hard cubes are a give-away, probably because the dies in the cuber are wearing out and rather than spend a fortune on new ones he's shovelling in more hardening agent. The snag here, from your point of view, is that over the prescribed rate some of the chemicals used can attack the ovaries and inhibit blood coagulation. If you have a problem with piglets with bleeding cords at birth, resulting in them dying or being excessively pallid, look no further. It's a problem which, when it goes away for no apparent reason, often leaves you and your vet in a state of thankful humility and profound ignorance.

Another way to augment merchants' profits is simply to add an extra 50 kg (110 lb) of barley to the ration, which dilutes the specification but is not obvious unless you have been talking to your old friend the independent analyst.

If you want to save money on food, stop wasting it

A source of temptation to some, especially if they have a handy wharf, is the offer of what in the trade are called 'distressed parcels' – loads of material that have overheated, gone mouldy or rancid, or been damaged in some way. If your merchant is infiltrating these into your rations, then your profits become distressed or, depending on which part of the pig cycle you're living through, your losses will increase.

Farm trials are another minefield. They're a nonsense anyway unless done on a long-term, strictly controlled basis. Even then it only wants a new chap one weekend to feed the wrong food once to destroy the trial's validity. To add variety to results, it has been known for 25 kg (55 lb) bags in fact to weigh 30 kg (66 lb), with benevolent effects on the results. A similar happy effect can be obtained by supplying trial food at a rather higher specification than that sold.

Lorry drivers are nearly all honest, upright characters but if you leave one to unload and stack the bags you might well pay for your neglect if he leaves a hole in the middle of the pile that will not be revealed by counting the rows. On bulk loads, make a practice of occasionally putting the lorry over a weighbridge before and after unloading. Once this is established, it will curb any temptation to leave a little in the lorry or drop some off *en route*.

When a tanker is being unloaded, make sure the contents are blown out at a moderate rate. If the lorry is hidden in a white fog and the driver is sitting in his sealed cab revving up his engine, it means he's late for his tea and the lack of visibility is costing you money. Other commonsense precautions are to compare the specification on mineral/vitamin supplements with the ADAS standards; if they are way below, they're being sold solely on price and you are getting what you pay for. There are ways to feed pigs very cheaply if you take the trouble to look, if you're operating on a reasonable scale and if you are clever at balancing rations. There is a vast amount of varied waste food available from food factories down to retail outlets. The other classic way of using waste food is to feed swill, where your food is either very cheap or free although the capital involved in preparation equipment is high.

First, if you want to save money on food, stop wasting it. On most farms the waste is 5–10 per cent – probably £5000 for every 100 sows. Second, don't cut the quality of the ration just to cheapen it; you'll lose two to three times what you save in lowered returns. Finally, use an independent analyst; if you don't know the right questions to ask, find someone competent with no axe to grind, such as a retired meal merchant, and pick his brains.

DO	**DON'T**
Be wary.	Believe in the free lunch.
Use an independent analyst.	Waste food.
Ask the right questions.	Cut quality to save money.
	Forget to consider using waste foods.

DIARY

Sunday 17th of April: Sunday feeding.

A pleasant feeling of moral superiority helps you over the first hour of feeding – it's a lovely morning and no one else is stirring. After the first hour, dust, noise and smell dull this feeling a little but it lasts in residual form until breakfast. The relatively little work left after breakfast goes quickly, nothing has gone wrong, the sun keeps shining and it's back to the Sunday papers and try and forget about cutting the grass.

I go out a little late for the shorter afternoon feed and at once meet a thought-provoking sight – a weaner. Nothing so remarkable in that, I hear you say, but weaners come in two-and-a-half dozens so there are 29 more enjoying themselves somewhere. First reaction is to put the 'pigs out' routine into operation and make sure all the gates are shut, next locate where they've come from and where they are now. A metal gate panel has given way and their present state is discovered by following a trail of dislodged brooms, buckets and general mayhem. They're in two groups plus a few stragglers, who 'woof, woof' in simulated alarm and helter-skelter off. They've had a lovely time.

So, rig up the hurdles to funnel them in, get a pig board and medium-size son Matthew and somewhat smaller daughter Rachel to act as long stops, gird the loins and start the sheepdog act. Half an hour later, and considerably hotter, they're all in their new pen bar a couple of agile malcontents; they can find somewhere cosy in the straw stack rather than me have a stroke.

It's still a lovely afternoon, nice for the beach or lazing in the shade with a long drink. I thank my excited helpers, return them to the house and turn to the afternoon feed again, much less placid and the feeling of moral superiority completely evaporated. Why do gates suffer metal fatigue only on Sundays?

A sniff of freedom

ILLNESS, DEATH AND DISASTER

It is no accident that this is one of the longest chapters. The first essential in sorting out trouble is to be able to recognize it. Ask yourself:

Will it eat and drink? The usual first symptom of an ill pig is that it stops eating. This can mean it is seriously ill. However, check the food to make sure it has not had its flavour modified by a careless piddler, and also check the water supply.

Has it an abnormal temperature?

Is there blood or obvious injury, perhaps bite marks or scratches?

Can it stand and walk?

Is its breathing laboured? (Is it breathing?!)

Does it make odd noises?

Is it an odd colour?

Is it scouring or constipated?

Are its actions unusual? Is it walking round in circles, banging its head against a wall or lying separate from its peers?

Eventually, you should not need to go through these questions but be able to look at a pen of 30 pigs and immediately pick out one that is ill or different.

The only way to acquire this level of expertise is to know instinctively what a normal pig looks like and this takes time. When that picture is fairly imprinted on your mind any abnormality stands out like a sore thumb.

Having identified your ill pig, what then? As a general rule, the younger the animal the less its stamina and resistance, so the quicker you move. Any piglet that is ill in the first few days of its life is usually a 'life-or-death' case, whereas adult stock are incredibly tough by human standards. Even so, it is always better to treat quickly. The longer you leave a pig in the hope it will be better tomorrow, the longer and more expensive will be the recovery and the greater the odds on chronic injury or infection. Find a 'good pig vet' if you're not sure or confident, and learn from him; it will be cheaper in the short run as well as the long.

If a pig is really ill, get it out by itself and make it warm and comfortable, except if it's been badly beaten up and is distressed. Don't try and move it, however inconvenient, or its heart may pack up; leave it where it is and move the others. A dead sow is expensive and a considerable bother to dispose of. Remember, though, if it's away from its peers for more than a day or so it will be regarded by them as a partial or complete stranger and they will most probably fight.

Coughing their hearts up

Cleanliness, if not Godliness, is one of the main factors in disease control. The others are stopping new disease getting in, good management practice and luck. Freya Stark once said of her travels in Tibet that you either take all precautions or none at all.

There are advocates of both extremes in pig farming, but those who take the most precautions tend to have the healthier pigs. The argument used by the opposite faction can be summed up by saying that as they have most of the bugs available they are no longer vulnerable. The younger the pig, the stricter the hygiene must be. As they get older, they develop resistance to most of the endemic problems on the unit.

Meticulous cleaning and resting of farrowing areas is essential to prevent disease build-up but the odd times when you're pushed for space a dry, dirty pen is preferable to a wet, clean one, especially in winter. It is irritating if you clean your pens like a hospital ward and still have trouble, while your neighbour who never does anything has none. It could be that you have an unappreciated management or housing problem. Simple things, especially if you are stuck with old buildings, can make an enormous difference to pig comfort and health and your profit. It depends on your ability to put yourself in the pig's place. Why, you should ask, are they always lying away from the bed area? There may be a piercing top draught that you'll only discover by sitting there yourself. The pig is stuck where you put it, remember, it can't go and get an anorak if it feels cold. If you decide to go mad and instal max-min thermometers, put them, protected, at pig level and not in a convenient place halfway up the wall.

It isn't easy to dispose of a dead sow

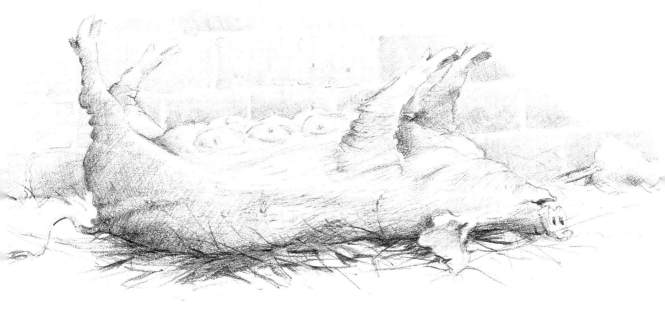

Again, spend time intelligently observing your pigs, and not just at feeding times.

There could be a temptation if your buildings and pigs are new and clean not to bother with pressure washing every time you empty a crate. At this stage the new pig-keeper, not having had time to develop many problems, may start wondering what all the fuss is about. It usually takes several years to realize how little he really knows, which is when the learning process starts in earnest.

It often happens that after a number of years a unit develops a financially crippling load of endemic disease. In a climate of ever-tighter profit margins, this presents the choice of doing something else for a living or clearing out and starting again with a higher health standard. If you stay with your old, evil habits, though, you could soon be back where you were before.

If you want to upgrade or maintain your health standards, the most effective way is to subject yourself to the discipline of a health scheme. You could do it yourself given the time, energy, expertise and self-discipline, but it doesn't always happen just like that. The most efficient and comprehensive organization is the Pig Health Control Association. This was set up originally to control enzootic pneumonia but now deals with other controllable diseases and afflictions. Its function, basically, is to test your herd to find the level or lack of a particular disease and to help you maintain that level. Their periodic inspection forms read like a tax return. (If the answer is 'none', write 'none'.) There are, rightly, no loopholes and your name on one of their lists is the best guarantee that at a particular date, though not necessarily after that, you were free of that particular disease.

Unfortunately, often the only way to rid yourself of a particular disease is to start again with new pigs with hopefully fewer problems. This is an expensive operation, involving loss of cash flow while the overheads trudge on. If you are starting a new herd, it would seem sensible to begin with as high a disease-free status as you think you can maintain. Remember the higher the status the more complicated your precautions must be, and the more often you wake up at 5.00 a.m. worrying. If you want to keep all your own genes use hysterectomy. You can either employ a veterinary laboratory to do this or do it yourself on the farm. For this you will need separate premises, a vet, a slaughterman, five other people and a decade to spare. It ages you ten years. It is not a procedure to be undertaken unadvisedly, lightly or wantonly, or by the novice pig-keeper – the pitfalls are many and varied.

The basic precautions for starting a 'disease-free' herd are as follows. 'Disease-free' is in inverted commas because there is no such beast. All it means is that on a specific date, to the best of your knowledge, the pig was free of certain specific diseases and conditions.

If you are starting on a new site, establish the herd as far from other pigs as possible. An area of low pig-density has fewer disease problems. You need a perimeter fence, ideally double, well outside the pigs, with only one access, which is supervised or under observation. This access should have means of people and vehicle disinfection, and a place to change into protective clothing. For vehicles, neither a wheel dip or soaked straw are any good in the long term. The straw gets muddy and the wheel dip, unless drained and refilled daily, becomes a wheel infection agent. It looks good, though.

Probably the most effective method is to wash vehicle wheels with disinfectant on the road. First, though, have a quiet chat with your vet on the actual efficacy of most disinfectants when they are actually used, as opposed to under laboratory conditions.

One very sick sow

Put your loading ramp and meal bins on the perimeter well away from buildings and again supply a means of disinfection.

Nothing will stop the occasional idiot from wandering in, but large, brutally frank notices will make most visitors pause. A scruffy 'keep out' sign is of little use. Non-essential visitors around the unit on a social visit are to be deplored; take precautions even if they say they've never seen a pig before.

The health dangers, in order of degree, are:

1. A pig from outside. The corollary to this is that if any of your pigs escape and temporarily vanish, they can't come back inside.
2. Stock lorries that may have other pigs on board, but have certainly been to farms and markets recently.
3. Your vet, who spends most of his time with other diseased animals. However, he will ensure that he doesn't go near other pigs for the necessary period before coming to you.
4. Your own staff, who must be educated never to go near other pigs or the local market, and to tell you if they accidentally do.
5. Food lorries, their drivers and salesmen, none of whom must penetrate farther than the farm office.
6. Yourself, who may go to pig meetings, demonstrations and shows involving possible pig contact. This means a bath and a hairwash before you go near your unit again.

Watch out for the multitude of people you don't normally associate with pigs: the electrician who has just wired your neighbour's farrowing house, the mechanic come to fix the automatic feed unit, the plumber, the party from the infant school (one of whose father keeps pigs) and the dustman. Be kind but stern and keep them out, but if they must enter, purify them.

Cats, rats and starlings are difficult to disinfect so should be discouraged. Sparrows, on the other hand, are territorial so don't exterminate them or your neighbour's sparrows will come in and colonize. Finally, check frequently that your precautions are actually happening and have not been quietly abandoned months ago when everyone was busy. This level of precaution is desirable, though not many pig farmers manage to stick to it. Of those who do, some still meet disaster, which teaches them to be suitably humble and not too dogmatic about anything to do with swine.

DO	DON'T
Learn the checklist of symptoms. Treat all illness quickly. Isolate the ill pig. Consider health schemes. Keep health dangers fresh in your mind.	Forget hygiene. Let warning notices get old and illegible. Get complacent.

Then there are the myriad improvements we'd like to make

DIARY

Wednesday 18th of May: Maintenance.

I counted them up once and we've got 253 gates and doors, each subject to continual abuse by pigs, humans, tractors, corrosion and acts of God, and that's just the start.

There are gutters and downpipes that block, break and collapse, windows that crack and shatter, walls that start to sway, cobwebs that obscure, ceilings that sag, taps that leak, ballcocks that jam and flood, and on and on.

Then there are the myriad improvements we'd like to make, like heighten a wall to keep an amorous boar frustrated. Every generation or so we get a boar that can leap like a gazelle and the walls get progressively higher and higher, which they take as a show-jumping challenge. Then there are ramps to improve, eyelets to fit in walls for hurdles, false ceilings to put over sows to keep them warm – or bulldoze the lot and start again. Most of these can only be attempted when a pen is empty and, if it involves concrete, empty for some days. Here we enter the realms of fantasy.

However, this afternoon we're going to devote a whole hour and a half before feeding to maintenance. This happens nearly every month, so where shall we start? It's no good starting something we can't finish, which will leave a pen out of action. And we need to finish the afternoon with some sense of accomplishment. This narrows it down to maintenance rather than repairs. Repairs and renewal we mostly leave to our two retired stalwarts, Hugh and Arthur, both skilled craftsmen and pig-wise, with the 'never screw it if you can bolt it' approach. The most cost-effective thing to do seems to be to haul out all the creep feed-hoppers and empty them of stale meal, which can be fed to the sows as a treat. We can then adjust and mend the slide controls to stop them flooding out expensive pellets to make a nice warm bed.

An hour or so later we finish, a bit dusty but with the necessary warm glow of accomplishment. We must do this again in a month or so if we can find the time.

HOW TO
CHOOSE A VET

If you keep pigs in Wales, among 10 million sheep, then the probability of finding a good, experienced pig vet within a commercial distance is slim. If you live in a high-density pig area, however, not only will there be plenty of vets who know one end of a pig from another, they will have treated, if not cured, a fair variety of pig diseases.

Unfortunately, as in every profession and calling, there are a few vets whose motivation, energy and ability are below average, and if there is one person you must have on your side, even more than a good accountant, it's a good pig vet. Choosing a pig specialist is important because the field of veterinary medicine is so vast that no vet can be a real expert in more than a limited range of species. It can be disconcerting, as we once found, to consult an expert on camels about suspected swine fever.

Ideally, you need a partnership where your vet comes on periodic discussion walk-rounds and otherwise you just consult him on the phone unless it's an emergency. You must, though, be prepared to pay for telephone advice. There should also be mutual trust so that he can leave you drugs for specific purposes, knowing you will only use them as agreed and keep a record. He should also abide by your disease-prevention routines as scrupulously as if he hadn't suggested most of them himself, and should reassure you on every visit that he is uncontaminated by other pigs.

A practice with three to five vets is useful, as you can always be fairly sure of having someone available who has not been near pigs that day. A vet who is a one-man band and under continual pressure does not get much time off to continue his education and keep himself up to date.

Distance is another important factor; he should be able to reach you quickly in a real emergency and it shouldn't take half a day to fetch some drugs from the surgery. Fifteen miles is about the maximum but this obviously depends a lot on the state of the local highways.

Sooner rather than later you will develop a problem your vet will want help with, so having good access to laboratory facilities and specialist consultants is highly desirable. It is also useful if he has a thorough grounding in the morbid economics of pig production. This will prevent him from embarking on cost-plus treatment of an economically worthless animal. Vets also tend to have big feet, possibly through having been trodden on by heavy beasts, so when you buy wellies for visitors get size 11s and large size overalls. Finally check occasionally that the boots are still intact. There is nothing which dampens enthusiasm for disease prevention so effectively as a boot-full of freezing disinfectant.

If you're in real trouble he'll come at once

When you ring your vet, give him a concise, accurate and low-key account of the problem. Try not to ring every time a pig looks uneasy; his quarterly bill will stop you doing this in time. If it's not panic stations, tell him so he can plan his day efficiently and remember to phone early, especially if you have disease-free status. Conversely, if you're in real trouble he'll come at once. Even vets must go on holiday sometimes, so when the newly joined young 'Herriot' arrives, instead of the one you know and have spent years training, be cautious but not resentful. He has, after all, spent years in arduous training, longer than a doctor – a sobering thought – and he's got to practise on someone.

Finally, should a trusting bank manager lend you money to build or extend your unit, consult your vet before you start mixing the concrete. He may well save you a lot of money for a lot of years.

DO	**DON'T**
Look for a good specialist pig vet.	Phone him unnecessarily.
Be concise and early when you phone him.	
Consult your vet on buildings as well as pigs.	
Try and follow his advice.	

DIARY

Tuesday 7th of June: Injecting.

There is no getting away from the fact that the back farm office is always grotty. It is the base for all expeditions into the real world of pigs and it shows it. Strange grafitti stain the walls where near-empty spray markers have been tested to see if they still have life, straw emptied out of revolting wellies lies in little heaps on the floor, and the sink is bright green where someone has been washing ear-marking equipment. The only clean part is the cupboard from which we're taking the hypodermics and needles and where also hang the AI catheters, drying lonely in the dark.

Sticking needles into pigs doesn't sound much fun for either side but practice, and thus dexterity, make it bearable for all. Grown-up pigs have usually had regular routine injections, so the problem here is anticipation. We walk into the sow pen, chatting to them cheerfully and holding the tray of hypodermics, markers and bottles of vitamin injection, a belt-and-braces precaution after a long, grey winter. This injection is a slower job than the one-second erysipelas vaccination as it's oil-based and has to be really pushed through the needle. The technique is simple: come up from behind on the left, a swift slap with the back of the hand to numb the skin and slide it one-handed into the neck muscle on the far side. This gives you the balance and control to do an elegant job.

The technique is simple

Except for one. She's been watching the whole process with an uncharitable eye and keeping the other side of the pen. Her we get a bit of help with, a handful of sow nuts on the floor – she's not fooled, but her mates pin her still as they rummage heads down and she's done at the cost of a stamped-on foot.

That's the sows done, now the boars. Injecting older boars is state-of-the-art stuff, especially if they have even residual tusks. Take a trusty companion, two pig boards and some food, remembering that he's got a hide like a rhinoceros and that you will definitely only get one chance. A new sharp needle helps. He's wary, too, but greed overcomes distrust and as his head dips in the trough you do a quick and painless job and thankfully out, leaving him still eating. A sneaky way with a really difficult boar is to wait until serving day. No iron injections today. Iron dextrose is a thick solution that has to be forced through thin needles into baby pigs. If the needle blocks and the pressure is sustained the apparatus explodes, giving a striking mottled effect to the surroundings which, as you've been leaning over it, are mostly your face.

PIG PEOPLE

You would think, would you not, that there are only a certain number of accidents that can happen on a pig farm – run over by a tractor, savaged by a boar, falling off or through a roof, or just falling over, all fairly humdrum.

Not a bit of it. Try, for instance, walking into an open slurry tank while looking the other way and then consider the social problems of the Good Samaritan who drives you home wrapped in paper sacks, and has to explain to his wife why her car smells different.

Consider the case of the same dear gentle pigman who fell off a bale stack hitting his head on the dumper on the way down and asked, as he recovered consciousness, if he'd damaged it. Or, would you believe, the metal grain silo which was totally live and the outraged pigman vibrating on the ladder acting as a 240 volt conductor to the ground. After the more interesting parts of his life had flashed past, he shook himself free.

The minor, day-to-day occurrences are the weighing-machine handle that responds to a bouncy pig by springing back and dealing you a savage blow straight up your nostrils, or three large sows trampling you underhoof as they trundle out of a narrow passage as you try to enter. Life is neither dull nor safe with pigs.

The farm accident book makes good reading at Christmas parties. There is only a small space for the description of the accident, encouraging a terse, laconic style: 'Hit on head by

foreloader bucket', 'Walked into upright sackbarrow in the dark
– bruised groin', 'Rammed projecting bolt into scalp going
through low doorway getting boar out of pen'.

Pigs seem to get a fair amount of police attention. Boar
deliveries at night in a big crate are guaranteed to attract the
curiosity of bored traffic cops. A sow sitting in the passenger seat
of a Bedford van going through the centre of Ipswich gets
comment and attention, especially at traffic
lights. Another embarrassing incident
is to set off to deliver a boar, and

Three large sows
trampling you
underhoof . . .

when you arrive and fling open the van door it's gone, leapt out *en route*.

The majority of pig people are diligent, hard-working folk who keep going through thick and thin and don't earn a fortune. Good husbandrymen and women are scarce, and getting scarcer, and this won't improve until a more prosperous industry enables them to earn more for their skill and long, unsocial hours.

Career prospects, a summary of the first 25 years

Year 1   A year of enthusiasm spending money on stock and equipment.

Year 3   Begin to wonder what all the fuss is about in this pig-keeping lark and why your fellows moan such a lot.

Year 5   Start writing short articles in *Pig Farming* telling people the correct way to keep their pigs. Equipment starts to rust, collapse and disintegrate.

Year 7   Begin meeting the normal problems everyone else has. Stop writing for *Pig Farming*.

Year 9   Read *Pig Farming* for advice from clever clogs in their fifth year.

Year 11   Probably now sufficiently knowledgeable to realize how little you know. Decide your buildings are clapped out and dated.

Year 13   Free weekends seem further apart. Sell the boat you bought five years ago to go sailing in your spare time.

Year 15   You could stand the pigs if it wasn't for the people.

Year 17   Develop the 'branching out into another type of livestock' syndrome.

Year 19   Decide there must be more to life than this.

Year 21   Conclude there is more to life than this.

Year 23   The next time the EEC turns maligant, you're out.

Year 25   Re-discovering evenings and the weekend.

DIARY

Monday 4th of July: Night-time.

The nightly walk-round becomes part of your life. The more extreme the weather, the longer it takes. In the bleak mid-winter, it's satisfying to leave them warm and snug while the wind howls outside. A friendly grunt, a nose sticking out of a pile of straw and small pigs slumbering in a heap under the glow of the infra-red lamp and the watchful eye of their mother. Being July, the dusk is warm and balmy, with bats careering round the rustling poplars.

Several are due in the farrowing house. It's silent apart from slow heavy breathing, then the silence is shattered by the uproar of a newly feeding litter and within a minute they're all awake and clamouring for food as they struggle for their teat and the sows grunt rhythmically. Eventually it tails off and silence tiptoes back. One of the new sows has started and already she has seven suckling hard. She'll need no help bar a quick look just before bed. Leave her and close the door quietly.

The night is when you look and listen. A quick flash of the torch into each pen and off quickly before they wake and decide to be startled. Using the torch has other perils; with night vision gone, you are easy prey to wheelbarrows and the odd concrete block.

Decide all is well and go back, blinking, into the light indoors.

A quick flash of the torch . . .

PURVEYORS OF BREEDING STOCK TO THE NOBILITY

To explain the grandiose title, most of the herds to whom we once sold breeding stock were captained by earls, dukes, lords, retired generals and air-vice marshals, and a sprinkling of knights, but pigs seem to have gone out of fashion with them lately. Assuming, however, that you're not one of the nobility, buying your first breeding stock will heavily influence the first years of your swineherding career. Your best allies for this purpose are an enquiring and sceptical mind, the right questions and your 'good pig vet'.

In the first flush of excitement, it is very easy to buy a couple of in-pig sows or a few bacon-size gilts from a neighbour. You can improve the quality, but you're stuck with whatever bugs and health level they bring with them, however pure and beautiful any subsequent stock may be. The only way to upgrade your health level then will be to clear right out and start again, something you will become financially and emotionally increasingly loath to do. Starting off fresh with clean or rested buildings is a rare gift, so don't squander it.

You never forget your first pigs. We started with Jezebel and her two daughters, local crossbreds. Jezebel was an old hand even when she arrived, long and heavy with a perky nose and a huge black patch over one eye that gave her the look of a blowsy, drunken old harlot. She was the mother of Screaming Skull and various other eccentric progeny.

Even before you start thinking about breeding stock, a

procession of enthusiastic gentlemen waving glossy folders will descend upon you, all claiming to have the perfect answer to your problems. How to sort the wheat from the chaff? First, beware of vast price reductions, which mean they can't sell their pigs because they're not very good, they're going bankrupt or they have cut costs by abandoning costly research and development and health schemes. Vast discounts off an already sky-high price are another ploy, to make you feel that you are being offered a fantastic bargain. Consider only the final figure, not the mythical discount.

Incredible performance figures need qualifying and a beady eye. How super-charged was the food? Are the buildings overheated? Over what weight range was the test? Look for test conditions that approximate to good farm practice; they're more likely to be repeatable by you.

Do not take a company at its own valuation. If you study *Which?* reports, the best-advertised product often comes bottom. Remember that the size and technical excellence of an advertisement relates to their advertising budget, not necessarily to their pigs.

Jezebel

Claims of infallible performance with stock should be treated with reserve. Something unexpected happens to everyone's breeding stock eventually; pigs are variable mammals produced by fallible humans. Your job is to pick out the people to whom it happens least often. Extra points to those who qualify their answers and don't make too many dogmatic statements. They've probably kept pigs themselves and have attained humility. They should also appreciate you don't have time to spend the whole morning talking.

Having provisionally decided on a shortlist of people you can trust, go and see the stock on the nucleus units. It's unlikely that you'll be allowed near the multiplying units further down the pyramid as they're not usually equipped for visitors, but ask anyway. If they treat you like a source of the plague and encase you behind a glass screen, it means they take health seriously. Bring your vet into the conversation at an early stage; ask if he can talk to their vet, and if they decline go away shaking your head. Ask also for the names of people near you who use their stock to help you assess whether it will suit you.

Now is a good time to find out their attitude to replacements, both from them and their customers. The normal procedure when an unsatisfactory animal has to be slaughtered is for you to return the slaughter value and them to provide a replacement. Even if this is agreed, the degree of haggle can vary a lot; ideally, let the vets adjudicate.

Always remember that performance figures and indices are not comparable between companies; there are far too many variables to make any comparison meaningful. All an index does is hopefully tell you how good a pig is in relation to any others getting exactly the same treatment in food, buildings and regime. Ask what the weighting of the index is towards the various selection factors and how they calculate it.

A word on buying boars. Don't succumb to the temptation to save by buying one of lower quality. The maxim that the boar is half the herd should be engraved across your chequebook. One point to remember: the same quality of boar, if you could identify it, could vary in price up to 30 per cent between different vendors.

Sadly, with a few notable exceptions, individual breeding herds cannot keep up genetically with the better breeding companies. Genetics is to do with number-crunching and pigs are inevitably, though more slowly, going the way of the poultry industry.

The best way to get the authentic flavour of the purveyors of breeding stock is to spend a day or even two at the annual Pig Fair. Although it happens in April, take wellies, warm clothes and possibly food; neither the weather nor the catering is overly reliable. You will see the stock the various companies consider their best and what they are striving to attain generally, so if you don't like the pigs they show you are unlikely to be pleased with any others. As a general rule, it's the pigs that take your eye that you do best with.

If you want to see the pigs looking fairly natural, go on the first day. By the second, they've been prodded so many times to get them to stand up and show their finer points that they need a bomb to move them. However, if they have any personality defects like an evil temper this will show up by then.

They've been prodded so many times . . .

Ultimately, there is no easy answer to buying stock. Pick the type of pig you like from people you feel you can trust, remember it's tomorrow's market you're breeding for and let's hope you get it right first time.

DO	**DON'T**
Ask the right questions. Beware glossy advertising. Ask for satisfied customers. Be careful comparing rival performance figures and indices.	Start off locally on impulse. Always go for the cheapest boar. Miss the Pig Fair.

DIARY

Tuesday 9th of August: Serving.

If the pigs' hormones have done their stuff, the sows should all be on heat today, dreamily clustered in a group as near to the boars as they can get. Unless, that is, it's the one week every year or so when nothing at all comes on heat and we get a double dose of farrowings in four months, three weeks' time.

Before we sally forth armed with pig boards and resolution, I've sorted out who is not related to whom and which boar line mates with which line of female. This is fine on paper, but there is also the delicate matter of physical matching – can the little, though admittedly eager, fellow reach, or can she, young and tender, support the weight? Luckily we don't have to bother with the emotions as a further variable; with the hormones in overdrive, all males and females are desirable.

This is not a job to approach with haste or urgency. Some boars have a long pause for chat and conversation before they get to the point, but there is no hurrying each particular ritual. The mature performers mostly dispense with conversation but make up for it with thoroughness and application.

One of the sows isn't quite on heat and we have to get her out quickly, fighting a heroic rearguard action with a lusting boar to gain time to slam his door and prevent a running battle round the farm.

No AI today. It introduces another dimension – whether the semen arrives on time or at all, entrusted as it is to BR or the Post Office. To be fair, it usually does arrive, but it's the failures you remember. AI really does need patience. It can take up to 20 minutes, which seems like an hour, half-crouched at the back end of a sow, and the temptation to squeeze it all in is extreme. However, instructional manuals say 'use gravity and let nature take its lengthy course'. Finished at last, we go and have a wash and coffee and hope the smell goes by lunchtime. All to do again tomorrow.

Potent but mighty Fred

A ROOF OVER
THEIR HEADS

A friend of mine once observed that a pig unit is an empire on which the concrete never sets.

Personal experience and prejudice, expert (and inexpert) advice, cost, location, climate, the customs of the district, a visit to the National Pig Centre at Stoneleigh – any or all of these could contribute to the place in which you may spend many industrious years. The first and absolute rule in accommodating pigs is to make everything four times as strong and durable as appears necessary. Pigs are riotously destructive and their waste products corrosive.

Remember that unwanted, out-of-date pig buildings have a very low re-sale value, except in the unlikely event of a boom in pig prices. Their yearly written-down value in your accounts is a nonsense unless you keep on using them.

To achieve a living in an increasingly competitive world, the buildings must be effectively insulated and ventilated, and achieve optimum production with minimum labour. If there is a choice, go for simplicity. Stop and consider how many thousand times each gate, bolt, flap and ventilator is going to be used on a routine basis. Now is the time to indulge in some basic time-and-motion studies which could save miles of plodding.

All this excellence will cost you an arm and a leg. If you only have limited cash, it might be better to put the emphasis on more or better breeding stock, which will be earning you money, rather than on depreciating expensive buildings. If you're young and fit and not employing labour, the way round this is to start with rackety old buildings and insulate them and the pigs with masses of straw. This is very labour-intensive, but if it's only yourself you can afford to work an 18-hour day. This has the added advantage that you don't need to decide on a more permanent set of buildings until later. Whenever you are tempted, remember that whatever you spend on 'dead stock' comes off that often narrow band between income and expenses called 'profit'.

One more qualification, and an essential one: there must be sufficient concrete and drains that work, otherwise you will spend your days in or surrounded by an evil-smelling swamp. Inspect or visualize the place in January. Once you have established that the drains work, where do they go? This is not a problem to be shelved.

Pigs are riotously destructive . . .

Unless you really know what you're doing, do not be tempted to do your own electrical work. Pig farms are dangerous enough places without adding a Russian roulette factor like dodgy wiring. Call in a qualified electrician.

85

Do not think, because the next house is out of sight, that you are fireproof. If there is a change in housing policy and a bungalow estate appears over the hedge, it's you that is going to be closed down even if you were there first.

The Water Board and local councils are becoming increasingly bad-tempered about pollution and the pig variety can be tracked upstream through miles of ditches and watercourses. Rainwater is fine but directly it mixes with pigs or filters down through your muckhill it becomes slurry, expensive and difficult to dispose of, especially on heavy land. Keep them strictly apart, even to the extent of putting a cover over your muckhill.

If you anticipate trouble, don't lurk behind your gate with a shotgun or write uncouth and defiant letters. Invite your local council health people to come and see you, show them some suitable problems and ask their advice. You will find that in general they are not devious bureaucrats trying to drive you out of business but hard-working, harassed public servants. If you really are being driven crazy by officialdom, get your local NFU representative to mediate as a start before you work your way from your MP to the European Court of Justice.

Try not to be in the absolute forefront of trendy thinking; wait a couple or three years until the faults have been ironed out by the more gullible.

Do consult your vet, as I've said before, in the early design stages or at least before the concrete has set. Most disease conditions can be modified or aggravated by housing design. Again, talk to him early. He may well point out something fundamental, like it's not a good idea to establish a breeding unit quite so near your swill-feeding neighbour. Another factor you might like to consult him on is the design of your sow houses. If pigs are in discomfort or unhappy, they don't do so well. You won't make as much money, or make less than usual. Eventually you'll go bankrupt or give up.

Having got your pig or pigs in place concern yourself with tackling the problem of sordidness.

There is no place quite as sordid as a sordid pig unit. The first rule concerns litter. Do not drop any of the following where you finish with them: baler string, paper meal sacks, muck forks, brooms, shovels, assorted tools, tractors, pig boards, building materials, buckets, discarded clothing. *Put them back* – or dispose of them out of sight.

Once you have started to keep this general mobile litter under control, begin the advanced anti-sordidness course by walking carefully round and removing to an appropriate scrapheap everything unnecessary to its surroundings. This includes choice articles such as sacks chewed off at pig height, abandoned building materials (especially broken concrete blocks), rusty, broken equipment hiding in rampant clumps of nettles, old broomheads and disgusting corners in mealhouses and store-rooms. Then there's the heap swept up by Fred three months ago in a fit of enthusiasm and left because it was lunchtime. Don't burn all the baler string prematurely; it's extraordinarily useful for 'temporary' urgent repairs.

Never spill food; if you do, sweep it up at once. If you can't, hide it until you can. Feed is around 80 per cent of a pig farmer's total costs. Further, such waste looks and is unprofessional.

. . . an evil-smelling swamp

Dispose of the body. Even the best-run units lose pigs, but they don't leave them lying around. So get rid of the carcase as soon as the vet or whoever has seen it.

Clear out the gutters if you have a free moment. In an average downpour, an acre of roof has to dispose of many tons of water and if the gutters are broken, sagging or sprouting a crop of indigenous greenery then the water will go in another direction than that originally planned, to someone's discomfort. The best time to look at gutters is when it's raining as if it means it, but this is not popular.

We are heading towards a time when it will become socially unacceptable to keep large and intelligent mammals, whose natural bent is to root and explore, closely confined in stalls and tethers for most of their adult life. Legislation on this will take years, and in the meantime good husbandry and some straw can often make well-designed stalls preferable to cold, wet yards, bullying and poor husbandry. A good gauge of a system might be having confidence to take your town friends around, suitably purified, on a Sunday afternoon.

The final immutable law on pig buildings and their equipment is Murphy's. If it can go wrong, it will, and if it can't, it still will.

DO	**DON'T**
Establish your criteria. Cut through the local bureaucracy. Keep things simple. Remember time and motion. Worry about pollution. Ask your vet about buildings. Remember Murphy's Law and that pig farms are dangerous places.	Neglect drainage. Be the first to try anything new. Forget the welfare factor.

The heap swept up by
Fred three months ago
. . .

DIARY

Friday 19th of August: Getting the sows in to farrow.

Pregnancy has nearly run its 16-week course and this week's batch must come in before the weekend just in case of surprises. If we missed one and she farrowed outside with her mates, they would have a slim chance of survival, though more this time of year. It's another bad way to start the week, trying to rescue cold little bodies from the churning feet of a group of noisy, hungry sows.

It's a measured and steady job, bringing in these ponderous and fruitful ladies, swinging their burdens from side to side as they walk ahead of us. Occasionally one will decide that no way will she go through a particular door. There is no point in strenuous 'heave-ho' so we try persuasion and bribery with food and, if she still won't, the hell with it and we put her somewhere else.

As each one walks into her pressure-washed, freshly-strawed farrowing crate, we give her a handful of food in her trough, to keep her interested up that end while we fix the back bar. It doesn't slide easily with 150kg (350 lb) of sow leaning thoughtfully back on it.

We don't turn the heat lamps on yet, they're not due for some days. It's pleasant with what casual content the sows accept confinement; the plus side for them is personal attention and three weeks' respite from the stresses of community living.

All settled in – now we have room in which this week's served sows can start their pregnancy.

Ponderous and fruitful ladies

CONCEPTION

Never trust the sharp end of an adult boar. He needs to have aggression and sex urge to do his job properly, but these same instincts when aroused make him dangerous and unpredictable, however experienced you are.

A few adult boars are just naturally evil and should be sausaged, however good their genetic potential. Eventually they will maim someone, probably you. The danger signs are chopping his jaws together, frothing at the mouth and pawing the ground. Don't stay and remonstrate! This unsocial behaviour is usually provoked by the smell, sound or sight of another boar, even the smell of one on your clothes.

The boar's style of fighting is the upwards, sideways thrust into his opponent's stomach, so adult boars should have their tusks removed periodically. They are razor sharp and if he gets you the first sign is your welly filling up with blood. *Always* use a pig board when handling boars. Preferably there should be two of you and never have two boars loose at the same time, however large the unit.

Having installed a paranoic fear of all boars, it should be stressed that most of the time they are friendly and chatty if treated in a civilized manner, i.e. not hit or shouted at.

The basic principle is always to take the sow to the boar, or he could be distracted by all the new smells in her place. Also she is easier to move out afterwards. As you take her in, put a couple of old hessian sacks on her back – boar's feet are sharp and a raw back can be a distraction.

Let's go back, though. 'How do I know when she is on heat?', I hear you ask. She will be the one standing stock-still as near the boar as possible, with dreamy eyes and ears flicking up and down, or strongly erect. If one is riding another, the underneath one is liable to be most on heat. Her vagina will be red and enlarged, though not invariably. Do not try and move her by pushing from behind or she will stand like a rock, convinced you are a boar trying to have your evil way with her. Slap her resoundingly round the shoulders with the flat of a pig board and temporarily jolt her out of it.

Boars, like people, vary in the build-up time – up to 15 minutes. Prick-eared and most hybrid boars are generally fairly single-minded with a refreshing lack of finesse, but pure flop-eared breeds can sometimes be infuriatingly dilatory. There is no way, though, that you can hurry him, so calm down and wait.

A few adult boars are just naturally evil . . .

Remember, also, a boar cannot see what is happening back there and is not necessarily fussy where he puts it as long as satisfaction is attained. Supervision and help to check he aims right is a good idea. Be gentle – his penis extended is worth about £15.00 an inch.

Use her tail and your knee to line up the working parts into position. If you are crouching down using your right hand, the sow will tread on your left foot with a combined weight of around 180 kg (400 lb) per square inch, which will eventually lead to the obscure syndrome of Pigman's Foot. Another thought to keep at the back of your mind to aid concentration is that the boar may drop off on top of you. Getting her out of the pen is fairly simple if it's been a full service, but you might have to move fairly swiftly if you are trying to get a sow who has just changed her mind away from a rampaging and highly unsatisfied boar.

One such time, when we were young and fit, my head pigman and I were getting a sow served in an outside pen. She wasn't ready so we roared her out of the pen gate held by a helper – the boar was old and evil – who then slammed the pen gate. We flung our pig boards over the wall and, as one man, leapt after them. Unfortunately, we got entangled and, as one, we fell back, minus pig boards, to rejoin one sexed-up, bad-tempered adult boar, in a pen 3.5 m (12 ft) square.

The helper said later, when he'd stopped laughing, that the memory of the next 30 seconds was something he would remember with pleasure all his life. Except at treasured moments like that, though, try not to over-react to a boar and make him nervous or flighty – he needs to keep his self-respect.

As in life, timing is all and two good services, 24 hours apart, should give optimum results.

You can, of course, always use AI (artificial insemination). You get to use more expensive breeding stock than you can normally afford and, once you're trained, you should get equal results. Timing is even more important with AI but, even if you get totally hooked on it, it's still sound practice to have a real, odorous live boar around to act as long-stop and keep things stirred up. The AI equipment is fearsome. The catheter, or artificial penis, is 45 cm (18 in) long, flexible red rubber with a left-hand thread at the end, sure to bring the house down in a 'my job' talk at your local Rotary Club.

A gentle word of caution – do the inseminating in a smallish pen with no low doorways leading from it. The sow often gets bored, it can take 20 minutes and you are no substitute for a clinging, heavy breathing boar so she's quite likely to walk off through the same low door, leaving you to follow scrabbling along on your knees.

If you want to make life really difficult and hanker after a challenge, try using deep-frozen semen. This is more an art form than a technique and two equally competent people can get wildly varying results. Temperature, timing and sperm viability are crucial. It's pleasant using it in summer, the overspill of liquid nitrogen keeps your feet cool, but be careful transporting containers; if you turn the car over, you'll have about 30 seconds to get out before your feet go brittle.

As one man we flung our pig boards over the wall

To show, in another way, how difficult conception can be made and encouraged by an enterprising company who knew a mug when they saw one, we once bought a serving crate whose purpose was to aid the mating of two pigs of different health standards with no contact beyond that which was essent- ial to the purpose. It was made of oak with green canvas around the sides and on top, which we soaked in lysol, as instructed.

For a challenge we put the crate in the middle of an area of concrete before we put the sow in it. In those days we had some 15 men on the farm. It took their combined efforts and there isn't much on a sow for 15 men to get hold of.

As boars rely on sight, smell and body contact when being social this boar looked a little baffled when we led him up to the contrivance. When persuaded to go closer, he made it perfectly plain that lysol didn't turn him on and stalked off.

Apart from this, like the lady who, when asked why she'd embarked on the interminable rail journey to Alice Springs pregnant, answered that when she'd boarded the train she wasn't pregnant, that sow had by then gone off the whole idea.

DO	DON'T
Watch for boar danger signs. Always use a pig board when moving boars. Take the sow to the boar. Be aware of the signs of heat in a sow. Check he aims right. Give at least two services 24 hours apart. Learn to use AI.	Have two boars out at the same time. Try and push an on-heat sow. Be in a hurry when serving.

DIARY

Wednesday 7th of September: Harvesting straw.

Not being addicted to slats and slurry, being in fact a muck-and-mystery unit, we need large quantities of straw bales.

In a good year, the barley straw is strong, yellow and sweet-smelling, a reminder all the rest of the year of summer to come. If rain afflicts the harvest and it lies getting alternately drenched and dried for weeks, it becomes a poor thing, crumbly, grey and mouldy, no joy to us or the pigs.

This year is a good year, the sun burns down, the arable manager is heard singing to himself and the straw gang has nearly finished the last field bar one. Today we're let off the leash; we're going out to lend a hand for a few hours and get some fresh air. The older tractors are used on this job and we roar off down the road in a cloud of diesel to fields we haven't seen since this time last year. When we get there, the smell of the new barley stubble and the wide horizons and the skylarks singing are like a tonic after the restricted views of our two acres of concrete. We should do this more often.

Give her a handful of straw

The bales are stacked in eights, one stacker on the trailer and two throwing up. Easy at first and we make the stacker sweat but it gets a bit more energetic as the load rises, until we can throw them no higher. The load tied down securely, we go back much more sedately to the Dutch barn where one throws off, one feeds the elevator and the third stacks up in the eaves. It gives a nice sense of accomplishment and feeds the squirrel instinct to see them safely in the dry. Easy for us, though, we haven't got sore hands and aching backs from weeks of it.

BIRTH

Signs of approaching birth are general restlessness, the udder dropping at the back and a change of texture of the udder surface – difficult to describe, but generally changing from loose and soft to tight and full. The vagina softens and enlarges and a few hours before birth milk can be drawn from the teats. Another infallible test is to give her a handful of straw. If she rakes it back with her forefeet as opposed to just chewing it, she's on her way.

Most sows farrow in crates to prevent 140–80 kg (3–400 lb) of sow flattening 1.4–1.8 kg (3–4 lb) of piglet, so the full ritual of nest-building is prevented. To satisfy her instincts and get her in a state of contentment, give her straw to chew and rake about.

Sows often get up during farrowing to lie down on the other side, which is when mass slaughter can happen. Help her to do this, though, if she's big and heavy and finds it difficult to get up; it usually speeds things up. But do not think that having got her up she'll just flop, or hopefully carefully lower herself down again, and you can go and have your supper. It's so nice standing up again that it could take 20 minutes, so shut the piglets in the creep under a lamp and leave her to it.

It can take anything from half an hour to all night to bring forth and a sow's reaction to the event can vary. The euphoric mum lies on her side chatting happily while her newborn are checked over, warmed up and have their eye teeth clipped. However, when you're not there, this state of drugged happiness can cause her to ignore the piercing screams of a piglet with its head sticking out from under and rapidly going purple.

Porcus homicidalis is another matter and fortunately rare. The symptoms may not show before farrowing and it is often her first pregnancy (they tend to end up as sausages before the second). The first sign is a *Jaws*-like attack on the first piglet to wander unsteadily near her head. If she farrows in the small hours, a mass grave will be necessary in the morning. If you catch it in time, a sedative injection will calm her long enough to get them all suckling and she may then behave normally.

Some sows, however, while accepting that 'O.K., they'll rear the damn things if they have to', will try to savage any foot, hand or object that wavers within reach, however carefully and non-provocatively it is moved. However good her projected performance, she must go. Meanwhile, with the vast majority, get them used to your voice talking to them and make a fuss of them occasionally. You then have their trust when you need it.

When the litter is born, cut their eye teeth cleanly with proper clippers (kept in spirit) to stop them tearing each others' faces. It is also good practice to give the sow a hormone injection, which contracts the womb, ejects any lurking cleansings and also temporarily stimulates the milk supply.

It's so nice standing up again . . .

The normal ration of cleansings is about 'half a bucketful'. If only a little is produced and/or she keeps straining and not producing, get your vet quickly – something is jammed and needs pulling out. A vast number of things can go wrong during and after farrowing, when the sow and her litter are at their most vulnerable. The most likely are an obstruction in farrowing and subsequently an udder or uterus infection, and in the piglets a digestive infection.

Do not delay treatment if you have, or even suspect, a problem. Anything that interrupts the ingestion and digestion of milk in a baby pig is very expensive. Their mother's milk is literally their lifeblood, a taste of which can turn a limp, wet, newly born piglet into a ferocious, competitive fighter for his rights. This is because at this stage their reserves are minute – the total blood supply is only 25 cc. At birth, they also have very low levels of iron and serum immunoglobulin. Iron you can inject, but the serum to give them their mother's immunity to disease can only get to them through her colostrum. The problem is that the level of colostrum in the milk drops 50 per cent in the first five hours, and after 16 hours it's more or less gone; some sows produce a lot less than others. Hence the inherited desperation of the struggle for milk.

The most common causes of death amongst baby pigs are disease leading to starvation and dehydration, then cold and draughts.

How to recognize trouble with the sow? First, get her up to eat at the normal feeding time, however comfortable she is. If she turns up her nose at it, it's highly likely there is trouble. Next take her temperature. Don't put it in her mouth; thermometers are expensive and indigestible. Shake the thermometer well and press it against the side wall of the anus. Normal is 101.5–103.5. It should be low after farrowing so, even if it's in the top of the normal range, beware. Third, check for any vaginal discharge and feel the udder for hard hot lumps. It should be soft and malleable.

Just to confuse you, she could be walloping her food back, have a normal temperature and have an udder like plank. At the same time, watch the piglets. A normal litter lies around stretching occasionally with contented smiles on their faces. If they are going thin, hairy and listless and honk plaintively for food, ring the vet with speed if you are not certain what to do.

The other thing to keep an inquisitive eye and nose alert for is the squitters, known affectionately to the pig-keeping fraternity as the 'scours'. They will die from this with no effort at all, due mostly to dehydration, their inflamed intestines being unable to absorb liquid. Treat this lack of fluid just as urgently as whatever is afflicting them. The smell usually gives you warning first, like wet cardboard and quite unmistakable. Ill or, more probably, not, tender loving care at this stage is never wasted.

Complicated post-natal nasties – mastitis, navel ill, bleeding cords, the whole agalactia syndrome, anaemia and all the other plagues lying in wait to destroy your piglets – we leave to weightier tomes, but a word on fostering. If you want to even up your litters, you usually move the biggest first (they're likely to be the fastest to establish a claim on a spare teat) but that won't necessarily take the pressure off any little miseries left behind. If you've enough litters at the same stage, put all the small ones on one sow. Don't overload a thin sow, though; if you have to in order to save piglets, wean them off early and put them on a sow ready for weaning in good condition. Strangely, spreading infection between litters doesn't often happen.

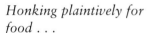

Honking plaintively for food . . .

Avoid draughts like the plague. All creeps should have an insulated lid and solid sides. If the litter is lying in a heap, even under the lamp, instead of being spread out, then they are too cold.

Finally, when you are picking up a piglet, don't grasp it round the shoulders or stomach. This will activate it's anti-crush warning system, the sow will leap up all concerned, the rest will wander underneath her and you'll be there 20 minutes. Instead, either pick it up by the back legs or slide your hand underneath its body, leaving the legs dangling. The difference is remarkable.

If all has gone well, you can enjoy one of the most rewarding things about keeping pigs – the sight, sound and smell of a contented, newly farrowed sow and litter.

DO	**DON'T**
Check on signs of approaching birth. Give her straw. Cut the piglet's teeth. Make sure they get colostrum. Check the sow after farrowing. Check and re-check the piglets. Think carefully when you foster. Avoid draughts and cold. Pick them up properly.	Delay piglet treatment if they are ill. Let them get thin or dehydrate. Forget that piglets are vulnerable and valuable.

DIARY

Monday 21st of November: Weighing.

Monday morning again and clearing up after the weekend, but our job is to weigh the pigs, the worst job of the week. It's got to be done today, the baconers go off tomorrow and we have to go through 48 pens of pigs. We also have an order for gilts and they must be selected. As well as selected, they have to be assessed and recorded and tagged ready for the ultrasonic operator tomorrow, who will record their back-fat depths. So we'd better get on with it. Fix up the scales and hurdles, select the best pig boards, tray with markers, ear tags, notebooks, pens, torch, wet cloth and soapy water, and we're ready.

It requires a burst of adrenalin

Start the first pen fairly relaxed – she's for bacon, cross on back, note the weight and out. The next one is a potential gilt. She decides she's not going in that crate and it takes a burst of effort and adrenalin to get her in. Record her weight, try and read the ear number – torch, cloth, crash with her head and she's jammed your finger, try the other ear with wet and now filthy cloth, yes, here it is, dry hands on overalls, write it, select tag and taggers, ear tag in and record it, mark her with a different colour and out she goes. While you're concentrating on this, other pigs are chewing your overalls, tripping you up and attempting to pee down your wellies. Another six or seven to check through in this pen, shut them in, drive the next lot out – 47 more to go.

Eleven o'clock, one house and a bit done, stop for a quick coffee. By now you probably hurt in one or two places – fingers, elbows or knees usually – your feet are cold and wet (in summer hot and wet), and you would definitely not be allowed on public transport. By twelve you start thinking that there must be better ways to earn a crust.

Starting again after lunch is slow because you've had time to stiffen up and your dry feet are not liking the cold, damp wellies. Also the swine see in your reappearance someone come to give them their afternoon feed. The 120 decibel uproar, pierced by a few ambitious screams getting up to 140, slowly subsides as they reluctantly give up the idea. By 3 p.m., the end is in sight and your glasses, and probably lungs, are covered with a thick film of dust. At last, the final pig – take the scales out, collect up the equipment and precious notebook. Have a quick count, 12 more than you had estimated and entered to go. Better rush back to the phone and try and get them booked in, otherwise the lighter ones, which you've marked as such, will have to stay another week.

Sit down thankfully in the office with the now disgusting notebook and write out the loading list. Discover you're in danger of nodding off in the warm. You've earned a cup of tea, so drop unspeakable overalls in a bucket to soak and plod heavily indoors.

GREEN PIGS

On one side are a lot of pig farmers working 16 hours a day, using the best technology they can afford and the government advisory services suggest; on the other, the general public, who quite like pork but would rather not know about abattoirs and have just seen the latest television documentary on factory farming. Meanwhile, the young lean towards vegetarianism.

Pig farmers do care about the welfare of their pigs. They even employ expensive consultants, for unhappy pigs do not thrive. Most farmers may feel uneasy about some of their buildings, but unless they win the pools there isn't much they can do about it.

Emotive documentaries often imply that if all pigs were put in grass fields in the sunshine universal bliss would follow. One of the most important things to remember in any discussion on animal welfare is the influence of husbandry, good or bad. Good husbandry can make the harshest conditions tolerable and, conversely, bad husbandry can create misery and stress in the aforesaid green field in the sunshine – even more in icy rain.

Generally, the smaller the animal or bird, the easier it is to concentrate in large numbers in small areas. Pigs seem to rest halfway between broiler chickens and bullocks. What offends most people are pictures of sows in stalls on slats or bare concrete and fattening pigs crowded in dark pens, and it is probable that within a few years the former at least will become socially unacceptable.

However, this does not mean that because some aspects of indoor pig-keeping cause concern that all pigs kept indoors come under the 'factory farming' banner. Pigs have been kept indoors to breed and fatten since history began, usually for very good reasons to do with climate, soil structure, bedding and, to a lesser degree, local tradition and cyclic fashion.

Outdoor pig-keeping has recently become popular again because if reasonable results are attained it is a cheap way of starting up and keeping pigs. The outlay on expensive and instantly depreciating buildings is minimal, so if you need to abandon pigs and flee the country your capital is available. Overheads are lower, pollution is seldom a problem and the soil is enriched.

Ecstasy

The qualifications are that you can only do it well on light land, pure sand being ideal. You can do it on heavy clay as long as you bring everything indoors before January begins to bite. You also need reasonably hardy pigs, which may be a mite fat, and reasonably hardy staff in a real winter under five feet of snow. The skills of keeping pigs outdoors being scarcer, staff are more expensive. This system normally only takes the pigs up to weaning stage, though a few farmers are fattening successfully outdoors. It is, however, a method of pig-keeping that is generally healthier, reduces stress on all concerned, is pleasing to the public eye and can be abandoned quickly if things get rough.

In richer arable areas where straw is cheap and available but land expensive, many pigs are kept in semi-intensive conditions on straw with natural ventilation. Where the climate is bleak and straw scarce, pigs are generally kept more intensively on slats with air flow and temperature controlled. This is, of course, a generalization: different systems merge and the different types of buildings overlap even on the same farm, let alone the same district.

New technology can bring back old systems in improved form. Pregnant sows are now kept in yards again with electronic tags round their necks. These let them feed on demand to the right level from (expensive) feeding units without the physical help of scarce stockmen, making sure they are fed the right amount and reducing competition and bullying.

One point cannot be emphasized too much. There is little point in making lists of welfare conditions for pigs if the people who are responsible for them are poor stockmen.

The RSPCA emphasize this in their new welfare code that they are developing. They make the point that 'welfare' doesn't exist on it's own. It's a much wider package covering training and behaviour of pigs and people. It also attempts to avoid being dogmatic and to translate vague generalities into understandable guidelines that pig farmers can adapt for use with their own ideas. Utopia, it accepts, won't come tomorrow.

Pollution is as big a problem on livestock farms as it is in cities. With outdoor herds, the problem is minimal; with straw-based herds, it varies depending on how near are the nearest houses and the prevailing wind. Muckheaps and their seasonal spreading come under the heading of normal country practice, but if you live next to several hundred tonnes steaming gently in the August sun you may wish to qualify that. If it drains into a ditch, the Water Board and the local council won't like it either.

Slurry is the real problem. A mixture of faeces, urine and a variable amount of water, the smell when it is spread is evil, though connoisseurs assert that chicken slurry has the edge.

There are strict regulations on its storage and leakage, which are only common sense if you want to keep any friends in the area. There is now also a method of spreading where the slurry is injected into the ground.

What is likely to lead to change in the next decade, bearing in mind the fallibility of all forecasts?

On pollution, we can expect draconian regulations to reinforce existing ones, which could well increase the trend back to straw-based systems. This also applies to antibiotic and other residues in meat. The EEC will control testing of samples nationally, plus local or farm testing. On the debit side, after 1993 it will become increasingly difficult to keep out Continental levels of disease, including rabies owing to the political and economic weakening of our veterinary defences.

On pig welfare, not a great deal will happen through regulation and decree, though there will doubtless be a lot of noise. The regulations that do emerge from Brussels will be left to individual countries to enforce.

Sacks chewed off at pig height

The factor that will most hasten change is consumer pressure. Supermarket antennae twitch at the slightest variation in consumer buying patterns and if the public want and are willing to pay for 'friendly reared pork' then we will soon be producing it. Meat-marketing is definitely consumer-driven. Supermarkets are already insisting on pork reared under a variety of disciplines and contracts. Some of these are quite good, some mean very little, but they all involve a handsome price increase. Unfortunately for pig farmers, since they have historically neglected to control their own market it is unlikely that more than ten per cent of the extra paid by the customer will filter back down to them.

Another interesting variable is the prospect of large imports of pork from a newly entrepreneurial Eastern Europe, possibly associated with the EEC, producing pork reared under a variety of welfare safeguards or none at all.

The Real Meat Co. in Wiltshire is an interesting development. It imposes sensible disciplines on its producers, maintained by independent random checks, and it sells directly to the consumer. It is still small but looks set to grow fast. It seems probable that this trend will continue so that, while at the moment it only affects a small minority of pigs, within a few years the rest may well have to take notice.

However, let us hope that in a world chronically short of food the niceties of meat production don't one day become academic.

DIARY

Thursday 22nd of December: Night farrowing.

It's Thursday night and the penultimate weeks' farrowings of the year are well under way, three have given forth so far and one looks very thoughtful, with milk coming well at the slightest touch.

The atmosphere is redolent of birth, the sweet smell of milk and wet new piglets and the breathless wrestling and jostling of rows of vigorous sucklers, taking in life itself.

With the main lights off, the infra-red heat lamps make a cosy glow round each litter, the shadows sharply dividing each crate in a cocoon of its own and throwing dark shapes onto the ceiling. As I walk behind, a quiet word to each sow to let them know I'm here so they won't be startled from their deep content. Here are a couple of small ones, part of a huge litter and submerged milkless in a bank of suckling piglets. Hold off five or six struggling little monsters and let the deprived have a chance at the front teats, and you see them suddenly quiver into life as the first milk flows into them. They'll have to be fostered off, though, they'll never survive among that crowd.

A contented sow and litter

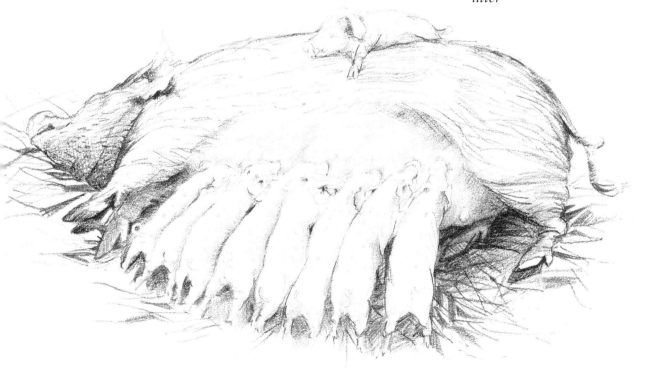

The next one looks like potential trouble. She has three huge piglets, obviously born some time ago, and she's straining heavily. Reluctantly with persuasion she gets up, has a drink and reflects before she lies down on the other side. That often helps to re-start things. Give her another hour – if no joy by then, it's a question of soap and hot water, stripping off and sorting out the obstruction.

Meanwhile, give the two sows who have finished an injection of pituitrin and cut the eight eye teeth of each piglet.

Eleven o'clock and the sow with problems has had no more, so back for soap, hot water and a towel. Soap the arm to the shoulder, lie down and gently work inside her, timing it as she strains. Here's the trouble, a large head in the left channel – work the fingers behind the ears and draw it slowly out. Good, he's breathing, clear his mouth and put him under the lamp. Better see if I can get any more, yes, here's a leg, get the other one and out he comes. Third time nothing, so leave her for the time being. She stands a better chance now.

Midnight and 10 big piglets and some cleansings; there may be one or two more but she can be left now. Give her some antibiotic as a prophylactic and some pituitrin to help anything remaining.

Check the others are content, that no more have started and to bed with a gentle glow of accomplishment.

GLOSSARY

AI artificial insemination
Ad lib feeder bulk feeder that enables pigs to eat to appetite
Agalactia a lack of milk in the absence of infection
ADAS the ministry Agricultural Development Advisory Service
Bacon size 90kg (198 lb) live weight
Catheter artificial penis for AI
Colostrum the first milk after farrowing, containing vital antibodies
Creep warm nest for baby pigs
Erysipelas an endemic widespread infection that affects the heart and joints
Farrowing giving birth
Farrowing crate device to contain a sow after farrowing to prevent her crushing her piglets
Gilt female up to first farrowing
Index a means of quantifying the total performance value, above or below the average
Killing-out percentage the weight you get paid for as a percentage of the live weight
Lairage waiting area for pigs at the abattoir
Mastitus udder infection
MLC Meat and Livestock Commission
Nuts hard cubes made from pig meal
Pannage right of pasturage
PHCA Pig Health Control Association
Pig boards small board for driving pigs, usually square and very dirty
Pituitrin hormone injection to aid ejection of after-birth and stimulate milk flow
Pophole low entry
Scours diarrhoea

Slats a floor with slits through which urine and dung fall to a channel underneath

Stalls a container for the pregnant sow

Stilsons a large spanner – a vital tool for all breakdowns

Tethers a half-stall where the sow is tethered by the neck

Ultrasonics the means of measuring fat depth on the live, and temporarily restrained, pig with a portable ultrasonic machine (as accurate as the operator)

USEFUL ADDRESSES

Agricultural Colleges giving pig courses. Refer to *Courses in Land Based Industries*, published by East Anglian Regional Advisory Council for Further Education, 2 Loams Lane, Bury St Edmunds, Suffolk, IP33 1HE. Tel. 0284 764977

Agricultural Development Advisory Services H.Q. (ADAS), Nobel House, 17 Smith Square, London, SW1P 3HX. Tel. 071 238 5631 (from here can be obtained a list of regional offices and pig advisors)

A. I. Centres. Try MLC head office for a list, although they are not involved with A.I. any more

Breeding Companies and pedigree breeders. Refer to NPBA

British Veterinary Association (BVA) (Pig Veterinary Society), 7 Mansfield St, London, W1M 0AT. Tel. 071 636 6541

Feed Companies. Refer to MAFF (publications), Lion House, Willowburn Estate, Alnwick, Northumberland, NE66 2PF, for their 'National List of Compound Manufacturers', ref. UR 150 BL 5813

Ministry of Agriculture, Fisheries and Food (MAFF), 3–10 Whitehall Place, London, SW1A 2HH. Tel. 071 270 3000

Meat and Livestock Commission (MLC), Head Office PO Box 44, Winterhill House, Snowdon Drive, Milton Keynes, MK6 1AX. Tel. 0908 677577 (ask for list of regional offices and services, also pig test unit at Stoneleigh)

National Agricultural Centre (NAC) (Demonstration Pig Unit), Kenilworth, Warwickshire, CU8 2LG. Tel. 0203 696551

National Farmers Union (NFU), Agriculture House, Knightsbridge, London, SW1X 7NJ. Tel. 071 235 5077

National Pig Breeder's Association (NPBA), 7 Rickmansworth Road, Watford, Herts. WD1 7HE. Tel. 0923 34377 (shortly to become The British Pig Association)

Pig Contract Schemes. List obtainable from MLC

Pig Health Control Association (PHCA), Dr R. Goodwin, Madingley, Cambridge. Tel. 0954 210500 (ask for a list of breeding companies and herds conforming to their rules)

Pig Processors, bacon factories, abattoirs,.etc. Refer to the MLC Procurement Organizations, to market pigs. Enquiries to The British Pig Marketing Society, c/o The Federation of Agricultural Co-ops, 17 Waterloo Place, Leamington Spa, Warwickshire, CV32 5LA. Tel. 0926 450445

Rare Breeds Survival Trust. At the NAC (see above)

FURTHER READING

Bell, Brian, *The Farm Workshop*, (Farming Press, 1992)

Brent, Gerry, *Housing the Pig*, (Farming Press, 1986)

Brent, Gerry, *The Pigman's Handbook*, (Farming Press, 1987)

English, Fowler, Baxter and Smith, *The Growing and Finishing Pig*, (Farming Press, 1988).

English, Smith and Maclean, *The Sow – Improving Her Efficiency*, (Farming Press, 1977, new edition pending)

Fraser and Broom, *Farm Animal Behaviour and Welfare*

Hoskin and Brown, *The Farm Office* (Farming Press, 1982)

Lampkin, Nicolas, *Organic Farming*, (Farming Press, 1990)

Sainsbury, *Farm Animal Welfare*, (Collins, 1986)

Seymour, John, *The Complete Book of Self Sufficiency*, (Corgi, 1978)

Straiton, Eddie, *Pig Ailments*, (Farming Press, 1988)

Taylor, David, *Pig Diseases*, (Farming Press, 1989)

Thornton, Keith, *Outdoor Pig Production*, (Farming Press, 1988)

Thornton, Keith, *Practical Pig Production*, (Farming Press, 1981)

Whittemore and Elseley, *Practical Pig Nutrition*, (Farming Press, 1976, out of print but your library will get it)

Not yet published, but watch out for John Gadd's comprehensive *Modern Pig Technology*, due out in 1993, and Longman's *Pig Health* from their Animal Health Series, due out in 1993.

MONTHLY MAGAZINES
Free to pig farmers

National Pig News   16c Market Place, Diss, Norfolk. IP22 3AB. Tel. 0379 650480

Pig Farming   Wharfdale Road, Ipswich, Suffolk, IP1 4LG. Tel. 0473 43011

Pig News   Journal of the National Pig Breeder's Association

Pig World   English Farmer Publications, 7 Strand St, Grimsby, South
   Humberside, DN32 7BC. Tel. 0430 810692

Free to NFU members

Pig Talk   Agriculture House, Knightsbridge, London, SW1X 7NJ. Tel.
   071 235 5077

By Subscription

Pigs   Missett International, PO Box 4, 7000 BA Doetinchem, The
   Netherlands

INDEX